"Luke?"

On impulse Christine entered the sitting room and stood staring at Luke's back. "I've decided to leave," she said in a low voice. "There's nothing for me to stay here for now."

An odd expression entered Luke's eyes. "It's Steve," he said. "He's the cause of the way you feel, isn't he?"

"No," she answered. "I don't love him. I know now I never did."

A long silence followed, and finally Christine left. Whatever it was Luke might have said would never be said now.

ANNE HAMPSON
has the same impetuous streak as her heroines. It often lands her in the middle of a new country, a new adventure—and a new book. Her firsthand knowledge of her settings and her lively characters have combined to delight her readers throughout the world.

D0030080

Dear Reader:

I'd like to take this opportunity to thank you for all your support and encouragement of Silhouette Romances.

Many of you write in regularly, telling us what you like best about Silhouette, which authors are your favorites. This is a tremendous help to us as we strive to publish the best contemporary romances possible.

All the romances from Silhouette Books are for you, so enjoy this book and the many stories to come. I hope you'll continue to share your thoughts with us, and invite you to write to us at the address below:

Karen Solem
Editor-in-Chief
Silhouette Books
P.O. Box 769
New York, N.Y. 10019

ANNE HAMPSON
The Tender Years

Silhouette Romance

Published by Silhouette Books New York

America's Publisher of Contemporary Romance

SILHOUETTE BOOKS, a Simon & Schuster Division of
GULF & WESTERN CORPORATION
1230 Avenue of the Americas, New York, N.Y. 10020

Copyright © 1982 by Filestone Limited and Silhouette Books,
a Simon & Schuster Division of Gulf & Western Corporation

Distributed by Pocket Books

All rights reserved, including the right to reproduce
this book or portions thereof in any form whatsoever.
For information address Silhouette Books, 1230
Avenue of the Americas, New York, N.Y. 10020

ISBN: 0-671-57178-8

First Silhouette Books printing October, 1982

10 9 8 7 6 5 4 3 2 1

All of the characters in this book are fictitious. Any resem-
blance to actual persons, living or dead, is purely coincidental.

Map by Tony Ferrara

SILHOUETTE, SILHOUETTE ROMANCE and colophon are
registered trademarks of Simon & Schuster.

America's Publisher of Contemporary Romance

Printed in the U.S.A.

Other Silhouette Books by Anne Hampson

Payment in Full
Stormy Masquerade
Second Tomorrow
The Dawn Steals Softly
Man of the Outback
Where Eagles Nest
Man Without a Heart
Shadow of Apollo
Enchantment
Fascination
Desire
Realm of the Pagans
Man Without Honour
Stardust
A Kiss and a Promise
Devotion
Strangers May Marry

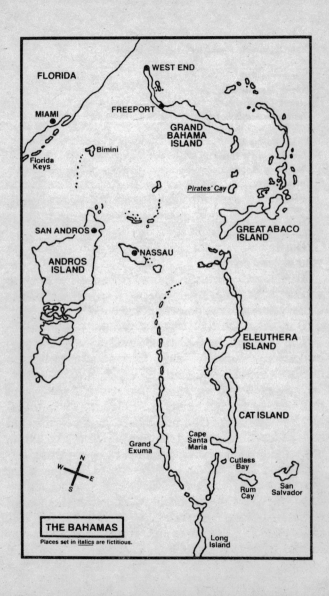

THE BAHAMAS

Places set in *italics* are fictitious.

Chapter One

The moment was charged with tension as the two girls, one pale with anger, the other inexpressibly hurt, faced one another across the room.

'But Greta, I *should* be one of your bridesmaids! I'm your sister!'

'Don't be so absurd. You've pretended ever since you came here. You're not my sister, so why you persist in the pretence I shall never understand!'

'But, Greta—'

'I've told you, several times, that I want only four bridesmaids, and as I have four best friends then obviously I can't have you!'

Christine stared at her dumbly; her big violet eyes had filled up and her mouth was quivering uncontrollably. She began to plead but choked on the words and had to stop. It seemed impossible to make Greta understand that the disappointment was so strong and deep that it had become a physical thing, tearing at her heart with crucifying pain. No, Greta could not understand because she had no ideas of sentimentality, of collecting precious memories . . . she was not an idealist like her adoptive sister and, therefore, could never be hurt in the way that Christine could.

'You—you c-can't do this to me!' cried Christine at last. She had pictured herself in a lovely flowing dress, proud to be the chief bridesmaid. '*Please*, Greta, let me be one of your bridesmaids.'

'For heaven's sake, when are you going to stop!'

'I've set my heart on it . . . please . . .' Christine's small hands were clenched against her breast. 'If you knew h-how it hurts you'd n-not be so hard.'

An exasperated sigh escaped Greta and a contemptuous frown marred her wide, intelligent brow. 'It's final,' she stated through her teeth, 'so don't go on any more about it. In any case, I want all blondes and you're dark.'

'Not very dark—' Christine glanced at herself in the mirror above Greta's dressing table. 'It's—well— middling, a sort of brown, but more honey. I'd be willing to bleach it,' she added, eyes lighting up as this occurred to her. 'Maria's great at changing the colour of her clients' hair!'

'For the lord's sake, will you stop this nonsense!' Scathingly Greta glanced at the girl who, having lost her parents in a road accident seven years ago, had been taken in by Greta's mother and father and treated as their own daughter, a circumstance which Greta had always resented but had, for the most part, managed to hide her true feelings from her parents. Not so with Christine, who knew the extent of Greta's dislike. Nevertheless, her decision came as a shock, for whatever was lacking between them, Christine had taken it for granted that she would be the chief bridesmaid at Greta's wedding. 'As if it really matters,' added Greta disparagingly. 'You'll be at the wedding.'

Christine looked at her through a mist of tears. Yes,

it did matter! Things like this mattered a great deal when you were eighteen, but she ought to have known that Greta would not understand.

'You're mean,' Christine could not help saying. 'I think that one day you'll be sorry for being so mean with me.'

'I'm mean?' with a lift of her delicately curved eyebrows. 'Well, if I'm mean, then you're ungrateful. You seem always to forget that you'd be in a home if my parents hadn't taken you in!'

'You always remind me of that.' Christine turned away, dragging her feet as she went towards the door.

'Close it after you,' snapped Greta, swivelling around on the stool to regard herself in the mirror. Beautiful! No wonder she had won the greatest prize on the island! A very satisfied smile curved her mouth as she picked up a silver-backed brush and held it thoughtfully for a long moment before beginning to brush her long golden hair. No real need for vigorous brushing; it shone naturally, as did her vivid blue eyes and her flawless skin. Yes, she was beautiful! Not like Christine with her dark hair which she liked to describe as honey-tinted, and her violet eyes. . . . True, they were large and expressive, admitted Greta grudgingly and with the appearance of a frown, but they filled up with tears far too often. Greta looked back four years to when she herself was eighteen. Was she a softie like that in her teenage years? The smile progressed to a laugh that was hard. No, she had never been anything other than practical, and she would get on in the world, whereas Christine and her like would end up married to some near pauper and live a humdrum existence until, when they were older and lost their looks altogether, their husbands would find someone younger and more glamorous. . . . 'Like me,' whispered Greta, who wondered just how long her marriage would last. No marriage lasted very long these days, but she must make sure she feathered her nest well before allowing any breakup to occur.

'Luke!' Christine saw the car and ran down the steps of the lovely white villa that had been her home for the past seven years. She reached the car just as it crunched to a halt on the gravel in front of the villa. 'Oh, but I'm glad to see you!'

Luke eased his long body unhurriedly from the driver's seat of his huge American car and Christine stood to one side as he closed the door before turning to look down into her animated little face. As always he found her enchanting, this fresh English girl who, bewildered and lost, had been brought out here to Pirates' Cay, one of the lesser-known islands of the Bahama group where Arthur Mead and his wife ran a flourishing business manufacturing Batik-printed fabrics, a great amount of which were exported to the States. Her uncle and aunt, several times removed, also English, had not hesitated to take her when her parents died, but although she had a luxurious home and a certain amount of affection from her adoptive father, Luke had always suspected that she was far from happy. Her eyes always gave her away and now, despite her smile and her lighthearted manner, it was her eyes that attracted and held his full attention. How well he remembered his first meeting with her, a child of eleven, bereaved and uprooted, brought here to a strange land, to live with people she had never met before. She had clung to him for some reason no one could understand, a slender mite who seemed to be drawn to him, and he recalled how her tears had fallen onto his collar and trickled down his neck, warm and fast flowing. He'd not had the heart to push her away despite the discomfort, and the embarrassment, for he was only twenty at the time and very conscious of the amusement of Mr. and Mrs. Mead, an amusement not shared by their daughter, Greta, who had stood there frowning sullenly, her pretty mouth compressed.

He had been uneasy, unsure of what he must do in circumstances such as these. His actions in the end came from sheer instinct; he held her trembling body close to his own, stroking her soft hair; he spoke soothing words against her cheek which, miraculously, eased her fears and pain sufficiently for her weeping to cease. It had been with a sort of wonderment that he had realised his success, had dazedly accepted that he had had the ability to comfort her. And from that moment there had been a bond between them so deep that, at first, Luke had never dared to analyse it.

'And how's my girl?' he said now, his observant gaze never leaving her face. 'Been crying?' Automatically his tawny eyes moved to the third window along . . . Greta's bedroom.

'No—er—well . . .'

'The answer's yes.' Luke could be stern when he liked, and his voice was edged with sternness now. 'Why?' he added briefly.

Christine hesitated, swallowing something that had lodged in her throat. 'It isn't important. You're here! And that is important. Have you come to see Uncle Arthur—Father?'

'Why have you been crying?' Luke was leaning against the car, one hand resting on the edge of the roof. Christine stared up into a face she loved, a handsome face in spite of the scar that ran down his left cheek, a scar caused when he rescued a child from drowning and injured his face on a jagged piece of coral, part of the reef. Luke was only sixteen then, and so shy that he just disappeared after handing the child over to her parents, a couple who were on holiday. It was several weeks before the truth leaked out. Now, Luke was anything but shy; he had travelled, had had a few affairs, and he had succeeded in business, having inherited two hotels on the island when his father died four years ago. Luke now had a third hotel on Grand Bahama Island and another in Nassau. Luke was refurbishing the former hotel and was buying materials for drapes and bedcovers from his friend, Arthur Mead. 'I asked why you were crying?' Luke's quiet, finely modulated voice broke into her reverie and she hesitated again, loath to explain.

His hand came out and her chin was taken, tilted in a way that had become familiar recently . . . for Luke seemed to have adopted a rather proprietorial attitude towards her these days. The result was that in some inexplicable way Christine's own manner had changed a little; she still knew the old camaraderie, but she felt also that he was too often her stern mentor and that she was obliged to respect and obey him. So now she found herself saying, almost against her will, 'I'm not being one of Greta's bridesmaids.'

'But—' Again his eyes flickered to the window of Greta's bedroom. 'What reason?' he demanded with a taut inflection.

'She has her friends. . . .' Christine bit her lip hard to help stem the tears that had again gathered in a cloud behind her eyes. 'I—I—'

'It's your right to be a bridesmaid,' he broke in angrily. 'The chief bridesmaid.'

She nodded dumbly, catching her underlip between her teeth. Why, oh why, did it hurt so much? She would be at the wedding as Greta had said, and wearing a pretty dress—'But it's not the same!' she cried in anguish before she could control herself. Words she had not meant to utter . . . she glanced into the eyes of the man still holding her chin, firmly, but yet tenderly for all that. She saw his fine mouth compress, the tawny eyes glint like metal.

'Greta has said definitely that you can't be a bridesmaid?'

'It's n-not important,' she said again.

But Luke was eyeing her with that stern expression and his voice was very soft as he said, 'Chris, answer my question.'

'She wants only her best friends—and blondes.'

'Blondes?' he repeated, frowning in perplexity. 'What has the colour of your hair to do with it?'

Christine thought of the many times he had visited here, often for dinner, and always he had looked at Greta's beautiful hair with admiration—but then, everyone's eyes were attracted to its luxurious colour and sheen, and its length, for Greta knew it suited her long and so she had it well past her shoulders.

'It would look odd if there were one dark head among the other blondes. . . .' She tailed off, aware that all this was having no effect on her companion. His face was hard, his eyes glittering with anger. Christine

13

hated him in this kind of mood. She craved his more familiar gentleness; she had always blossomed in the warmth of his smile.

'I wish,' she said, again without due thought, 'that you had been my guardian—my adoptive father.'

'You do?' The inflection was as unfathomable as his changed expression. He seemed to give a small sigh but what his inner thoughts were Christine could not imagine as all he said was, 'Consider me as your adoptive uncle, then.'

'I do—always have, but . . .' Her voice trailed pensively. 'If you were my guardian . . .' A sigh and a smile, a hand coming up from her side to remove his from her chin and then to seek the warmth of his clasp as she wound her fingers into his palm. 'Shall you be here for the wedding?' He was away quite often, usually on business, but a few weeks ago Greta had informed Christine that he had a glamorous girlfriend in Miami and that was why he went there so often.

'Does my answer mean a lot to you, dear?' He knew it did, at this time of disappointment over the matter of the bridesmaids.

'You said you weren't sure of being here,' Christine reminded him as she bypassed his forthright enquiry.

'I intend to be here,' he said and his reward was a swift spontaneous smile that brought a glow to her eyes.

'Lovely! Will you dance with me?'

'Of course, several times.'

'You always treat me as an equal.' She stopped as she recalled again his proprietorial manner with her recently. He was beginning to make her feel inferior and she wanted very much to find a way to stop it.

'Why shouldn't I treat you as an equal?'

'I'm so much younger—nine years.'

'Yes,' he murmured inscrutably, 'nine years. It's a lot. . . .'

Before Christine could say anything a cheery male voice was heard and they both turned at once.

'Steve.' Christine looked down at her feet, almost snatching her hand from Luke's. 'I didn't expect you today.'

'No? Greta did, though. She wants me to take her out to lunch.'

Of medium height and with a fresh complexion, Steve Walworth, Greta's fiancé, was more rugged than Greta would have wished and Christine knew it. But to her Steve was perfection . . . everything a girl could wish for. He was manly yet kind, considerate and, in spite of his great wealth, of a homely disposition—he liked puppies and kittens, babies and old people. To Christine he seemed totally unsuited to her sister, for where she was hard and materialistic, he was soft and seemed to have a sort of contempt for money. He had always been charming towards the girl who would soon be his sister-in-law and sometimes Greta seemed jealous of the relationship.

But she had no need to worry; Steve adored her, treated her like a queen. He had never seen the unattractive side of her because she was an excellent actress. Even Luke, with his keen perception, had no idea just how malicious Greta could be.

'It'll not be long now,' from Luke, who had not missed the effect Steve's appearance had had on his young friend. Calf love, he mused. She would suffer but get over it.

'No, not long,' agreed Steve wryly. 'I shall be glad when it's all over. Can't stand ceremony and people watching me.'

Christine lifted her eyes to look at him, a flush slowly spreading over her face at her own intimate thoughts. Steve sailed a lot; he loved boats. So his skin was bronzed and weather-beaten; Luke's was equally bronzed but not as toughened. There was a certain superiority about Luke not seen in Steve, even though Steve did possess a certain air of dignity and self-confidence—not always in evidence but there all the same. Steve's eyes were deep set and shrewd, while those of Luke were more penetrating in their shrewdness. Christine felt sure that if it were he who was engaged to Greta, he'd have seen through her long before now. She gave a deep sigh, feeling sorry for Steve but more sorry for herself. He was her shining example of what a man should be but it hadn't been until recently, when the wedding was almost upon them all, that she had realised just how much he meant to her.

'I'd better go and find Greta,' Steve was saying, a smile in his vivid blue eyes—eyes so like Greta's but yet lacking the hard glitter which Christine so often saw when she and her sister were alone.

'Where are you lunching?' Luke enquired and Christine shot him a glance of surprise. 'I'm asking,' explained Luke on seeing her expression, 'so that you and I will not arrive at the same restaurant as Steven and Greta. The lovers don't want company.' Sarcasm? Christine suspected so but couldn't be sure. Luke often baffled her these days.

'You're taking me out to lunch?'

'I think it will do you good—cheer you up a bit.'

Steve cast her a glance. 'Do you need cheering up, then?'

She shook her head, hoping Luke would not say anything about Greta's attitude in not choosing Christine as one of her bridesmaids. 'I'll go and change,' she said and sent Luke the kind of glance he could not possibly misinterpret.

'Steve ought to have been told,' he was saying half an hour later as they were approaching the Country Club Restaurant, a delightful place looking out to the smooth aquamarine sea and several other islands floating in it—or appearing to. 'He'd have had a talk to Greta—'

'It wouldn't have made any difference,' broke in Christine, wanting to forget both Greta and Steve just now so that she could enjoy Luke's company and the lunch he was going to buy her. She had changed into a cotton skirt, short and full with a sun top to match—white with navy-blue bindings on the hem of the skirt and the neckline of the top. She wore her hair brushed to one side and held in place with a small white bow.

Luke had seemed to heave a great sigh when on seeing her he had said, 'You look eleven again. When, dear, are you going to grow up?'

She had looked at him in a puzzled way, for it did seem that he spoke impatiently and really there was no reason for it that she could see. He might have been *eager* for her to grow up, she thought . . . *waiting* for it. Christine had dismissed the idea simply because not only was it silly but there was no logical reason for it.

'I certainly would have made sure that you were a bridesmaid,' Luke was saying in response to her comment. 'And I rather think Steve would, too, if he knew of your disappointment.'

Christine shrugged and said, placing a hand on his arm after he had stopped the car close to the entrance to the Country Club, 'I want to forget the wedding, and just enjoy myself—with you, dearest Luke.'

His smile was slow to come, and faintly bitter, she thought, and wondered why.

'Dearest Luke? Am I your dearest Luke? Are you sure?'

She moved her hand away and frowned as she did so. 'You're different these days,' she told him. 'We used to be like—well, like brother and sister.'

'You said I was regarded as your uncle,' Luke was quick to remind her.

'Well . . . yes, in a way I did, but when we're together like this I feel like your sister.' She paused and waited but Luke merely switched off the engine and leant back in his seat. 'Do you feel like my brother?' she asked.

He turned to her with a wry sort of expression on his face. 'No,' he said quite firmly, 'I do not.'

'Oh, well, never mind.' Another pause and then, 'What do you feel like, then?'

'Kissing you—'

'Kissing me? You've kissed me often, but only when I've been upset.'

'Aren't you upset now?'

'I've recovered, temporarily,' she assured him, remembering that he sometimes described her behaviour as volatile. 'I just want to be happy while I'm with you. After all, we don't often go out for a meal—not on our own, that is.'

'I must put the omission right,' stated Luke as he slid from the car. He was at her side before she could even open the door and he helped her out, his hand warm and strong beneath her elbow.

She looked up and her eyes were glowing. 'What would I do without you, Luke?' She tucked her arm into his. 'I need you so.'

He made no reply, but as he turned his head to look at her she had the impression that he was saying to himself, 'We need each other. . . .'

What was the matter with her lately? She seemed always to be imagining things.

They entered the restaurant to nods of recognition from the waiters who all knew both Luke and Christine. Arthur Mead sometimes brought his wife and daughters here; it was his favourite eating place. Recently, though, Greta hadn't been with them, as she and Steve went off on their own, as was to be expected with a newly engaged couple.

'A table in the corner,' from Luke who hadn't booked because he'd made up his mind on the spur of the moment. 'And we'll have a drink first, in the restaurant.'

'The lounge is crowded,' observed Christine. 'So I'm glad we're having our apéritifs at the table.' She was fighting to put her disappointment from her mind, and fighting also to put Steve from her mind. She hadn't yet thought of what she was going to feel like at the wedding; she dared not.

Luke's gaze was perceptive and faintly troubled. 'I think it will be a good thing for all of us when this wedding is over and the couple have gone from Pirates' Cay for good.'

Silence. The wine waiter arrived and Luke ordered a martini for Christine. Her feelings were mixed regarding Steve's decision to live in Nassau.

'With lemonade,' he added and ordered a double whisky for himself.

'A double!' blinked Christine. 'You never have a double. In fact, you don't often have whisky at all.'

'Today, my child, I feel the need of that particular kind of sustenance.'

'Why?' she asked briefly. Had his love affair of which Greta had spoken gone wrong?

'If you don't ask questions, Chris, you won't be told any lies.' With a hand lifted to suppress a yawn, Luke picked up a menu and began perusing it. Christine frowned darkly at him, wondering greatly at his mood. Morose? Mentally she shook her head; Luke was never morose. He had a logical and set approach to life, taking whatever came along and putting it down to fate. She could never imagine him straining at the reins, becoming discontented with his lot. And yet. . . . Of late he had given the impression of some underlying yearning, some almost desperate reaching out for something just beyond his range. She looked at his face again, as he read the menu, noticing the firm and noble thrust of the chin and matching strength of the jaw; the mouth was full and, she realised with a little shock of surprise, had an element of sensuality about it she had never seen before, or ever expected to see. It was tight suddenly as she watched. What thought had come to him in this instant? she wondered, and unwanted colour filtered into her cheeks as he glanced up from under dark lashes any girl would give a great deal to possess. He had caught her unawares, caught her doing . . . what? His lashes flickered with the movement of his tawny eyes and she lowered hers swiftly, for there was some emotion within her rising for him to read if he had the smallest chance to do so. What was this quivering so close to her heart?

'What were you thinking just now?' he asked, lowering the menu but holding it open in both hands. She noticed his fingers, long and lean yet sensitive, like those of a pianist. She knew their strength because he used to lift her and toss her into the air, then catch her, saying she was little more than a doll. Eleven, then twelve . . . and then her teens and the beginning of real pleasure and pain, the ability to suffer, to be happy beyond words, to laugh or cry . . . no wonder Luke said she was volatile. Sixteen and Luke coming and going in her life as he had done for five years but now he had begun to treat her as an adult and she liked it. He had taken her out in his yacht, taken her to Nassau with him on three occasions, with the casual permission of her uncle and the more reluctant agreement of her aunt. Sometimes Christine wondered if her adoptive mother disliked Luke. As for Greta's opinion of him . . . she said little but looks spoke volumes. Nevertheless, she managed with her innate charm to attract and although Christine felt sure Luke had never had a crush on Greta, he had never once, by word or glance, shown anything but amicability. Christine rather thought his attitude towards her would have been one of indifference had it not been for his friendship with her father.

It had begun when Luke's father had begun buying materials from Arthur, and this practice had been carried on by his son, for without doubt the designs produced by Arthur's company far surpassed any others on the market hereabouts. The friendship had grown despite the difference in ages; Arthur trusted Luke implicitly, hence the reason why he allowed him to take Christine off on these trips to Nassau. She'd had wonderful times, being taken out to dine with the kind of escort who attracted attention from every female around, old and young alike. Over six feet tall, with the sort of lithe and powerful physique that spelled sex appeal, he also possessed a full measure of maturity in spite of the fact that he was only twenty-seven years of age even now. At twenty-four he had been endowed with perception and common sense envied by many of his older business associates; at twenty-five he had made an astute and most profitable deal when he bought the hotel on Grand Bahama, and a year and a half later a similar deal was successfully carried through and one of the largest and most luxurious hotels in Nassau became his property. Christine had thoroughly enjoyed his company and his attention; she was flattered by it and she blossomed because of it. From the chrysalis of childhood emerged the beautiful imago—at least, Luke considered her beautiful, she knew. His opinion differed from that of her sister, who disliked brunettes anyway.

He was speaking into her recollections, asking again what she was thinking about.

'Us,' she replied and a lovely smile broke as her eyes met his across the table. 'The things we've done, and the things that you have done. You're clever, Luke, and you'll be a millionaire before you're thirty.'

'Does money matter?' His gaze was curious and it was examining. He missed nothing about her—never did. The smile that gave a glow to her big violet eyes, the way her nose turned up a little at the end, the slant of her lashes so that her eyes seemed almond-shaped, the wide clear forehead with its halo of honey-tinted hair and that unruly little half fringe which, having caught the sun, was shades lighter than the rest of her hair. Her skin too was affected by the sun so that it was the colour of honey-gold and gleaming with health.

'No, money doesn't matter,' she answered after a pause. But then she added thoughtfully, thinking of her adoptive father and his assiduous attention to his business, which she was sure came first in his life, 'It seems, though, to be a mark of success or failure, depending on how much you have made in your life.'

'You're referring to Arthur?'

'Yes, I was actually.'

'He gives almost all of his time to his business—to the pastime of making money. That's what you were thinking?'

She nodded, picking up her glass to sip the martini and regarding Luke from above the rim. 'He's giving all his life to it so I don't suppose you could call it a pastime.'

'All his life . . .' Luke paused in thought and a slight frown knit his brows. 'But then, he has little else in life, has he?'

It was Christine's turn to frown. 'He has a lovely home and a family.'

The straight brows lifted a fraction. 'You of all people should know he isn't happy.'

Christine looked down into her glass. She had suspected it but had never been quite sure. . . . 'You mean Mother—Aunt Loreen?' Why had she never been able to decide what to call her adoptive parents?

23

'It isn't a unique case by any means.' Luke returned his attention to the menu but she knew his mind was elsewhere.

She said guardedly, 'Have you any proof, Luke? I mean, it's an awful suspicion to have, isn't it?'

'I have no actual proof. As for the suspicion—you must have had it for some time?' The menu was lowered again but now a waiter was hovering, pad in hand, and Luke handed her the menu.

'Have you chosen?' she asked.

'I'll have a steak Diane. It's always good here.'

'Yes, they make it hot. I'll have it too.' She handed the menu to the waiter, watched him write the order down after asking about starters.

When he had gone Luke said, 'Surely it affects your life in some way?'

'I've always been conscious of what they did for me, Luke, and so I'm grateful all the time. I have a lovely luxurious home and Father loves me, I'm sure, so I haven't really troubled myself with anything else.'

'By that you actually mean: *anyone* else, don't you?'

She nodded after a slight hesitation. 'Yes, I suppose that is it,' she agreed.

'Loreen's always out, and what of these holidays she takes and the cruises? What does Greta think about it?'

'She never says anything. Greta has so many diversions, as you know, so many friends, which means she has a very full social life.'

After a moment Luke said, with a returning frown, 'How did we get onto this kind of subject? Let's change it. Are you coming over to Nassau with me next week?'

Her eyes lit up instantly. 'You'll take me?'

'I have just asked you, silly.'

She laughed, saw a nerve pulsate in his cheek and sent him a puzzled glance. But all she said was, 'If Father says I can, then I'd love to come with you. I love Nassau. I'll look forward to seeing your hotel there.'

'You'll like it,' he assured her.

'Are we sailing there?' she wanted to know.

'I think we'll fly. I haven't a great deal of time to spare. I have to be in New York on Friday week and then I'll fly down to Miami where I have to stay for a few days.'

'Miami . . .' Where, Greta maintained, Luke's glamourous girl friend lived.

Something like a pain touched her heart. For the first time she did not like the idea of his having a girl friend. . . .

Chapter Two

Over two hundred guests attended the wedding, which was to be talked about for weeks to come. Arthur Mead did not do anything without attempting to achieve perfection. He had a marquee on the lawn in case it rained but the sun shone through the entire day. It was a typical Bahamian wedding, held out of doors with the actual ceremony being on the extensive patio beside the ornately shaped swimming pool, where on the blue water hibiscus flowers floated, and magenta bougainvillaea, the petals looking like miniature yachts because of their shape. Hummingbirds hovered over flower bushes and other birds sang or twitted. A clear blue sky above the tropical scene, gay colours of the clothes and as many blacks as whites in the congregation as the wedding ceremony proceeded. Tears stung Christine's eyes as she looked at the bridesmaids and Luke slipped an arm about her shoulders, uncaring of who was behind them or what anyone would think. He drew her so close her head was on his shoulder.

'I love you for being so kind,' she murmured, trying to keep her voice steady in spite of the choking sensation in her throat.

'And I love you, dear, for being you.' His lips

seemed close but now her eyes were shut as she
endeavoured to hold back the tears.

'She looks so beautiful.'

'The loveliest bride ever on this island.'

'Steve's nice. She's lucky.'

Comments heard around her and no one seeming to
notice that Christine wasn't one of the bridesmaids. She
looked at Steve and closed her eyes again, for the pain
was excruciating, as she had known it would be.
Conscious of Luke's hand tightening on hers she turned
and pressed to him again. What would her life be
without the comfort Luke could always give her? Now
more than ever she needed him, but somehow the
words she wanted to voice just would not come. She
managed a smile, though, as the congregation rose to
sing the hymn. She and Luke seemed all at once to be
two people apart from the throng whose whole interest
was the bride and groom—the bride mainly; she stole
all the limelight, but then she always did, with her
flawless beauty, her stately poise, her inordinate self-
confidence. Steve seemed to be holding himself aloof
and Christine remembered his saying that he wished it
were all over.

The pronouncement . . . And Luke's hand tightened
on Christine's.

'Well,' he said prosaically, 'that is that. Are you
ready for the eats?'

She shook her head, watching as Steve kissed the
bridesmaids in a courtly kind of gesture, and all the
while he seemed to be looking around and at last he
was making his way towards Christine, leaving the
cameraman standing there behind him.

'Why weren't you a bridesmaid?' he said bewilderedly. 'What happened to make you refuse to attend your sister?'

Christine stifled the gasp that leapt to her lips. She looked appealingly at Luke because she had no words with which to answer Steve.

'I think,' said Luke in tones so brusque that Steve stared at him in surprise, 'that you had better leave any questions about that until another time.' He gestured abruptly. 'You should be over there, having your photograph taken. They're all waiting for you.'

A moment's pause before Steve turned his head; he had been watching Christine and could not miss the quivering lips, the brightness of her eyes. His mouth went tight, then relaxed at once. He reached for Christine's hands and drew her to him.

'A kiss for the bridesmaid that wasn't. . . .' His lips were warm on hers; she knew her own were cold, like her heart. Steve spoke close to her cheek. 'You look lovely, child. If I hadn't been marrying Greta, I believe I'd have waited for you.'

The colour ebbed from her face; she stared into his blue eyes and it was only by Luke's swift and perceptive action that she was saved from the impulse which would have resulted in untold humiliation afterwards, when she thought about it. Luke pulled her away a split second before she was about to fling her arms around Steve's neck and return his kiss with passionate intensity.

Luke and Christine dined at the Country Club, on their own.

'We oughtn't to have left,' she said as she took a drink of her wine. 'It must have looked very bad.'

28

'They'll probably not even have missed us in that crowd,' was Luke's unconcerned rejoinder. 'Watch yourself with that wine. You've never drunk it at that rate before.'

'We can have another bottle, can't we?' she suggested, eyes going to the bottle in the cooler. 'We've almost finished that one.'

His glance was as stern as his voice as he said, 'That, miss, is your last. I don't want to have to carry you out of here.'

'I need to get drunk,' she stated petulantly. 'I have a lot on my mind!'

'You're almost drunk already,' he observed. 'Eat your meat.'

'I have things on my mind,' she repeated. 'Didn't you hear me?'

'What things? The wedding's over and so you can begin to forget your disappointment over the bridesmaid business. I daresay you'll be a bridesmaid many times in the future.'

'I have other things to forget.' She picked up her glass again and emptied it. The room was beginning to spin. It was nice to be light-headed, she decided, since it made you forget all your troubles.

'Such as?' He was watching her curiously now.

She spoke, and said something she would never have said had she been sober. 'Steve. I love him.'

A silence followed and she saw Luke's mouth compress, his face lose a little of its colour—and that nerve again, pulsing like that. What was causing it?

'Calf love,' stated Luke almost harshly.

'I loved him at first sight.'

'Tomorrow you'll regret this confidence.' Luke lifted

a hand to fetch the wine waiter. 'Another bottle of the same, please.'

Christine bit her lips. 'I'm sorry, Luke. I don't really want any more. I've had too much already.'

'I intimated it a moment ago.'

'You're encouraging me,' she accused. 'Have you some ulterior motive?'

'What kind of motive?'

'I don't know.' She giggled and was lost for a moment. 'I'm tipsy, Luke, and it's your fault. You haven't taken care of me like you always do. What is Uncle going to say?'

'He'll probably put you across his knee.' Luke cut himself a piece of steak and put it in his mouth. 'You're still not eating,' he observed.

She was listening to the Bahamian music played by four men on the dais at the end of the room. 'I'd like to dance,' she said suddenly. 'We'd have been dancing if we'd stayed at the reception. You promised to dance with me, remember?'

'Were you in the mood for dancing?' he enquired dryly.

'I am now. Wasn't it super dancing at your lovely hotel when we were in Nassau? It seems years ago.'

'It's less than a month. Would you like to go to Grand Bahama?'

'Now?' Her eyes lit up, then shadowed again immediately. 'I've to go to work next week. I start on Monday as you know.'

'What made you get a job?'

'It's time. I'm eighteen and can't be a burden any longer to my uncle.' Besides, a job would take her mind off Steve, she thought.

'He doesn't want you to go out to work.'

'He told you?'

'Yes, as a matter of fact, he did. I promised to have a word with you about it, try to dissuade you. However, now isn't the right time by any means. Have a drink of water.'

She frowned at him and pouted. 'I'm not being ordered about by you, Luke!'

'You'll do as you are told. I've asked if you'd like to go to Grand Bahama. I shall be over there for about ten days.'

'Yes, I'd like to come with you.' Christine fingered her empty wineglass. 'I might as well have some more,' she decided. 'It's a special day, isn't it?'

Luke poured her a glass of water and pushed it across the table towards her. 'Drink it,' he ordered and after a moment's glowering defiance she did as she was told.

'Why have you ordered another bottle of wine?' she wanted to know.

'Because I need it myself.'

'*You* need it? Luke, you haven't a thing on your mind!'

His smile was faint and slightly bitter. 'How do you know?'

'It's obvious. . . .' Her voice trailed away as she remembered something. 'Is it your girl friend?' she asked, her voice slurring a little.

'Girl friend?' he repeated frowning. 'Which girl friend?'

'Have you more than one, then?' She looked up as the waiter came to empty the first bottle of wine. He poured her some and Luke made no demur; she wondered if it had escaped his notice.

'No,' he answered brusquely, 'I do not have more than one!'

'You do have one, then?'

He nodded his head. 'How do you know about Clarice?'

'Is that her name? Greta didn't tell me. She said she lives in Miami and she's glamourous.' Christine picked up her glass and took a drink which almost emptied it.

'So it was Greta, was it?' No particular expression, and even if Christine's mind had not been hazy she still could not have read anything from the fixed mask of his face.

'Yes, it was Greta. Luke, I want to dance—I've already told you!'

'Finish this course and then we'll dance.' His eyes examined her flushed face. 'No, we won't dance. I shall take you home.'

'I don't want to go home. I want to dance!'

'Chris,' he said sternly, 'you're going home!'

Tears started to her eyes. 'Do you have to be unkind to me today of all days?' she asked in complaining tones. 'I'm heartbroken and now even you turn on m-me. . . .'

'For God's sake, don't start to cry here!'

'Then be nice to me.'

'It looks as if I've been too nice to you.' Reaching over he removed her glass to his side of the table. She had to watch his glass being filled from the new bottle.

'Can't I have some—?'

'No,' he interrupted with an ominous glance, 'you can not, so stop being so silly and eat your dinner!'

Her lip quivered and her head was beginning to ache. She wanted to be in bed and yet, conversely, she hated the idea of going home, into the house which Greta had left forever, Greta who was married to Steve. . . .

'I'll eat it, but afterwards . . . I want to go to your house, Luke, not my own.'

'My house? You can't do that and you know it.' He stopped and drew an exasperated breath. 'Why didn't I stop you after the first glass? Hurry up and we'll go,' he said roughly. 'You're not having a dessert so you can forget your crepe suzette for this time.' He watched her profile as she turned her head in a petulant action meant to annoy him. His patience was becoming exhausted and he could have slapped her if they hadn't been here, in the restaurant. Yet in fairness he had to admit that he was mainly to blame; he'd had no need to allow her a second glass of wine, and then another half a glass. But she had seemed so forlorn, so caught in the net of her own dejection, that he had turned a blind eye to the effect the wine was having on her. And now she was much worse than he had at first believed; he wondered if he dare take her home—not that he feared the anger of her father. No, it was her mother he was worried about, Loreen, who had never shown any deep affection for the daughter of her husband's cousin twice removed. She had agreed to take her because at that time she was in love with Arthur, but now . . . No, not only now but for about five years . . . Luke had said he had no proof of Loreen's infidelity because he hadn't been able to betray a confidence, the confidence of the woman's husband himself. For Arthur had told Luke some time ago of the collapse of his marriage, but had said he would never agree to a divorce. And in fact Loreen did not want one; she had the best of both worlds—a lover and a husband, this latter providing all the luxury to which she had become used and without which she could never exist.

'I want my crepe suzette!' Christine's pettish voice broke his musings and he looked at her across the table, noticing again her flushed face, the disconsolate droop of her mouth. If she were to be scolded tonight by her mother, there was no guessing what the result would be. Christine could run away—anywhere. She could in her present state of mind act irrationally and Luke was not allowing that to happen.

But it took him some considerable time to make a decision. It was not easy but he knew it was for the best. 'Excuse me,' he said and rose from the table. 'I'll not be long.'

She watched him go, then beckoned to the waiter. 'More wine please,' she said and her glass was filled up. She knew this was all wrong, but she felt reckless. Her head was light and it made her forget her disappointment. More important, it made her forget that Steve and Greta would be in their hotel room by now. Forget? No, but at least the picture was vague; she could not see them getting into bed and making love.

'More wine,' she ordered after draining her glass. 'It's very good.'

The waiter was troubled; he glanced around for her companion. 'Perhaps, miss, you should wait.'

'What for? Fill my glass, please.'

With a sigh of resignation he did as she bade him, shaking his head as he watched her drink. Arthur Mead's daughter had never drunk much at all on her previous visits here, he thought.

Luke, meanwhile, had managed to get in touch with Arthur on the telephone. He explained that he and

Christine had been wining and dining rather too well, blaming himself for the way Christine was. 'I know it's highly irregular,' he went on, 'but I feel it would be best for the child if I took her home to my place and let my maid, Janet, take care of her. I feel she'll be better able to face Loreen in the morning.'

'Is she drunk?' demanded Arthur angrily.

'By no means,' hurriedly and with no remorse for the lie. 'But she's tipsy and I would hate to risk her being scolded by her mother. She's still brooding over this business of the bridesmaids, as I think you will know.'

'Yes, it was a damnable trick for Greta to do to the child. I said my piece even though it didn't suit either Greta or her mother. Well, if you feel it's for the best, then take her home to your place. But what shall I tell my wife?' he added in a faintly troubled tone.

'Need she know?'

A small pause and then, 'No, I don't suppose so. She never takes enough interest in the child to know whether she's in the house or not.' If it occurred to Arthur that this in itself made it simple for Christine to be brought home and put to bed without her mother knowing, he did not say anything, and neither did Luke.

When he returned to the table his face darkened with anger. 'I should have told Richard not to give you any more!' He gestured for her to stand up, which she did, but began to sway immediately.

However, Luke managed to get her to the car without arousing the attention of other diners, but when he arrived at his villa she was fast asleep and he had to carry her indoors.

'Mr. Curtis . . .' Luke's manservant stared and

shook his head in a gesture of deep concern. 'Sir . . . has Miss Christine been hurt?'

'No, she's not feeling too well, that's all.' He stopped on noting the sudden skeptical expression on the good-natured black face. 'John,' he said with a sigh of resignation, 'you are quite right; she drank a little too much at the wedding.'

'She isn't used to it, Mr. Curtis, so why did they let her have too much?'

'How much is *too* much?' Walking over to the couch, Luke laid her down, fixing a cushion beneath her head. 'As you say, she isn't used to it, but at a wedding one cannot be watched, can one?'

John's dark eyes flickered and he opened his mouth to say something but closed it again. When he presently did speak, it was to say curiously, 'Why did you bring her here, Mr. Curtis?'

'Because her mother doesn't know how—er—ill she is—' Luke stopped abruptly and frowned. 'There'd be a lot more sense, John, in your getting some black coffee.'

'At once,' agreed John and left the room. Luke stared down at the young face resting on the cushion and a small sigh escaped him. She stirred and her long curling lashes flickered, casting alluring shadows onto cheeks that were now pale and a little drawn.

'Oh . . .' She turned and would have fallen off the couch if Luke had not stepped forward and pushed her back against the soft, cretonne-covered upholstery. 'I feel awful. What happened—?' Her eyes searched his face before flashing around the room. 'I'm with you, Luke. I love it here,' and with that she snuggled down, put a hand over her eyes to shield them from the light, and would have fallen asleep again but Luke bent to give her a little shake.

'John's bringing some black coffee and you'll drink it, understand?'

Christine managed to sit up, supported by Luke's arm. 'John—what does he think?'

'He thinks you're drunk—'

'Tipsy!' she flashed indignantly. 'You had no right to tell him I was drunk!'

'I didn't need to. He's not without perception.'

She stared into eyes that were hard and stern. 'You're angry with me but it was your fault!'

'Careful, Chris,' he warned in a dangerously soft voice. 'My patience is not likely to stretch much further. I ought to spank you, and I might just do that if you don't take a grip on yourself and stop this childish behaviour!'

Her eyes sparkled. 'You're suggesting I'm putting on an act?'

'Not altogether, but you are being extraordinarily stupid.'

She coloured hotly and turned away, pushing his arm from her back. 'You're being unkind again. Have you no sympathy for me?'

'The past is gone, Chris,' he said brusquely, 'and there's no profit in continuing to dwell either on the bridesmaid business or on a man you can't have.'

She seemed to flinch at his last words. Her voice had a hollow quality as she asked, slowly and painfully, 'What time is it?'

'They'll be in bed,' was Luke's brutal reply and this time she shivered convulsively. It was the first time Luke had been really brutal with her and she knew a tug of pain that hurt in some mystifying way that was out of all proportion. Tears brimmed in her eyes; she had sobered miraculously and did not need the coffee which John brought in and set down on a small table by the couch. He had brought a full pot and asked if he should pour Luke a cup as well.

'No, thank you, John. Just pour Miss Christine's.'

It was done and she sipped the steaming liquid without protest, her tear-dimmed eyes still fixed upon Luke's austere face. 'I don't know why you're like this with me,' she complained at length when the silence became unbearable. 'Are you not friends with me any more?'

He moved away, towards the window where the drapes were wide open. Outside was the kidney-shaped swimming pool, illuminated from underneath, while all around it was the patio, covered with green all-weather carpet. Along the house wall earthenware pots and bronze containers held a variety of exotic plants— palms and allamandas, bird of paradise and angel's tears, while among the lovely climbers were the jasmines and the delightful bougainvillaeas. Bushes of hibiscus ranging in colour from deepest crimson to palest pink were easily visible in the lights trained down from the tall pines which were the natural vegetation of the island.

'Are you not even speaking to me?' Some inexplicable fear began unfolding within her as Luke's silence created a tension she could not explain but which was making her exceedingly uneasy. She had become so used to having him to lean upon that she had taken for granted the gentle care, the tenderness and the concern he had so freely extended to her since ever she could remember. Often she had wept on his broad shoulder, had snuggled into the haven of his arms, had poured out her heart, her innermost feelings. And if he should change towards her, should withdraw all that she had accepted as if it were her right . . . 'Luke, why are you so quiet?' The plea had its effect and he swung around, hands deep in his pockets. She looked at him, still immaculate in the off-white tropical suit he had worn for the wedding, his mouth and jaw set and stern, his eyes unfathomable in their masklike immobility.

'Drink your coffee,' he ordered and she knew for sure that this was not what he had intended saying to her. She obeyed, then slid from the couch, her dress, calf length, falling in folds which in some way accentuated the tender curves of her body. Luke's mouth moved as if in a convulsive way, and that nerve was there again, she noticed, pulsing spasmodically as if an outlet for some violent emotion.

She came to him slowly and even though he stood immobile, with that forbidding expression on his face, she did not falter, and on reaching him she wound her arms about his neck, lifted her face, her lips parted in a smile. Still he did not move and she became aware of renewed fear growing and flourishing within her. *Where would she be without him?* This austere silence was too unbearable! The narrowed, discouraging coldness of his eyes.

'Luke . . . please . . .' Her tone was constrained; there was an irresolute moment before the onrush of desperation which impelled her to seek his lips and crush her mouth against them. The startled second, the angry exclamation, the repressive stiffening of his body . . . And then she was swept almost savagely into his arms, kissed so fiercely that she began to struggle for freedom. Luke had no mercy when at last she managed to gasp out a plea for release; he was master and he let her see it. His hands roamed, exploring her lovely curves, holding her breasts possessively, caressing delicate and hypersensitive places, arousing within her emotions she was experiencing for the first time in her life.

'You've asked for it, Chris!' His voice was low and hoarse, coming from lips hot against her slender white throat. 'I tried—and you tempted—'

'I'm sorry!' she gasped, 'and I'm frightened! Let me go, Luke—I didn't m-mean to tempt you—' But it was too late; he had gone too far. Her head was forced back by the passionate strength of his kiss; her body was being brought to submission by the erotic caress of his hands.

'You shouldn't have asked to come here!' he told her almost savagely. 'But as long as you did, then you'll take the consequences!' He swung her right off her feet and strode to the door.

'Luke—what—?'

'Shut up,' he ordered roughly. 'I'm not made of stone. . . .' His voice trailed as the door opened before he reached it and John was there, his trusted Jamaican servant whose loyalty had more than once been proved.

'The room, sir—I've had Janet get the west spare room ready.' His expression remained wooden as he added, 'I see you are having to carry Miss Christine. I'm sorry, sir, that she is still—er—unwell.'

Luke's lips were tight and for a moment servant and employer stared hard at one another. And then a slow smile broke over Luke's face. 'Thank you, John for seeing about the room. I'll take Miss Christine up at once.'

'And I have instructed Janet to see to her, Mr. Curtis. For obviously Miss Christine will need help to undress and get into bed.' Still the wooden expression remained.

Luke said quietly, 'You think of everything, John, even the chaperoning service. Remind me to give you a raise.'

'That, sir, is not at all necessary. I merely do what I consider necessary.'

And with that he made a slight bow, opened the door wider and watched as Luke passed through with his burden.

Chapter Three

Christine awoke to the light of a new day pouring through the thin lacy material of the drapes; she heard birds chirping, a dog barking in the distance. All came back with a rush of embarrassment and shame. Luke! What must he think of her—? She stopped her thoughts, then switched them. Luke. What had he done? Worse still, what would he *have* done but for the intervention of John? John who was bent on protecting his employer, preventing him from an action he would by now have been regretting.

The blood was surging in her cheeks as she slid from between white linen sheets and approached the dressing table without even glancing around to examine the room and its luxurious furnishings. She was in a diaphanous nightgown which, she thought, must belong to Janet, the Bahamian girl who had worked for Luke since she was sixteen; and now she was almost twenty. Christine was naturally familiar with all Luke's servants since she was a regular visitor to his house. She had never been in a bedroom till now, however, and the memory of how she came to be here was something she would recall with shame and embarrassment for the rest of her days—or so she believed at this particular time.

She looked at herself critically; she had grown up yesterday and last night and now she felt different, a little more self-possessed and sure of herself. But she knew she would still continue to lean upon Luke, and could only hope he wasn't angry with her because of what had happened last night. Surely he would keep in mind that she had been tipsy? His reaction, though? She was puzzled by it, even though she was not so naive that she didn't understand just how he had been tempted. The wedding and then the dinner, this by candlelight in the romantic setting of the Country Club Restaurant. The wine—which must have affected him too; the drive home in the moonlight and with the breeze of the island wafting perfumes and pine scents into the car. The necessity of carrying her into the house; the final temptation when she had gone to him in desperation and kissed him even while he was determinedly resisting her. Yes, she now realised why he had been adopting that rigid and forbidding attitude. He had been guarding himself and her . . . but finally his resolve had broken down and it had been her fault entirely. She had regarded Luke as a sort of uncle for so long that she had allowed the fact that he was a virile man to escape her altogether. Now, though, she saw him in a different light and she was earnestly determined to take more care in future.

She bathed and dressed, and it was as if she had fallen into a state of limbo because she had no qualms about facing Luke at the breakfast table until she was halfway along the corridor and she caught the whiff of bacon and toast. She stopped, aware of warmth in her cheeks, dampness in the palms of her hands. She turned and would have fled out to the garden but John was there, a smile on his good-natured face.

'Mr. Curtis is waiting, miss. Please come this way.' Deliberately he was making it impossible for her to escape, since she had no alternative than to follow him to the breakfast room. Luke was already there; John silently withdrew and closed the door behind him.

'Sit down,' invited Luke as if knowing she'd be too tongue-tied to bid him good morning. He had risen and with the old familiar gallantry he was drawing out her chair. She thanked him in a low voice and sank down, keeping her eyes averted. Where, she wondered, was the new confidence she had earlier believed she had acquired? 'You look much better this morning,' he went on to observe with a cool appraisal and an impersonal tone to his voice. 'How do you feel? Not affected by a hangover, I hope?'

She shook her head. 'No—I feel fine.'

'Good. Then you'll eat a good breakfast before I drive you back to Cassia Lodge.' There were grey flecks in the tawny eyes which lent a metallic quality Christine had never noticed before.

'Luke,' she began, knowing that what happened must be mentioned if their relationship were not to be impaired. 'Last night—'

'Yes?' casually, but the very fact of the interruption gave evidence of his interest in what she had to say.

'I'm sorry. I was really tipsy. Forgive me for something which was entirely my fault.'

'Your generosity is most gratifying,' returned Luke sardonically. 'Many thanks.'

Christine's violet eyes flashed. 'Sarcasm's not clever!' she told him spiritedly.

'You're growing up, Chris. You used to treat me with respect.'

She felt deflated and lowered her eyes. 'I still respect you,' she asserted. 'I always shall.'

'Then don't give me any more of your back answers. I haven't yet spanked you but that's not saying I never will. I'm not used to receiving sauce from anyone, so remember that and take care.'

Christine glanced at him suspiciously. 'You're trying to avoid the issue of last night,' she accused.

'Issue?' with a blank expression that infuriated her. 'What issue?'

'Oh, Luke!' She subsided into silence and concentrated on the grapefruit which had been put before her by John, who had silently entered the room carrying a silver tray.

'Shall we forget last night?' suggested Luke when his servant had gone. 'I know that neither of us is proud of our behaviour and, therefore, it's easier on our consciences and self-respect to pretend it never happened.' Luke dug his spoon into his grapefruit and put a segment into his mouth. He was not looking at her and his indifference angered her inexplicably. She ought to be glad he was taking this attitude and could not for the life of her understand why she was not greatly relieved by it.

'It's difficult to pretend it never happened,' was all she could find to say, and this was after a long pause.

'I shan't find it difficult.' He shrugged. 'After all, it was not a unique occurrence, was it?'

'For you—perhaps not,' she agreed, hoping she was

not revealing her embarrassment. 'For me, though—yes, Luke, it—it was the first time I have—have ever had an—an experience like that.'

The tawny eyes flickered with an unfathomable expression as the slowly spoken response came through. 'I'm happy to hear it, Chris. Don't let it trouble you, dear—' His hand was suddenly covering hers as he reached across the table. Their eyes met; she found herself affected by strange vibrations as her pulses quickened. Bewildered, she cast her eyes down, reluctant to let him see her expression in case it should reveal to his perceptive eyes the turmoil that was affecting the nerve centres of her mind.

'It does trouble me,' she whispered eventually. 'You see, your opinion is the most important thing in my life.' So frank the admission, so anxious the look she presently gave him, that he rose from his chair to come round and place a kiss on her forehead.

'Child,' he said gently, 'you have no need to fear my opinion of you, not ever. I've known you a long time, remember, and we've been close. I could never think badly of you.' His gaze was direct and compelling. 'I want you to remember that always, Chris. Promise me you will.'

A lovely smile broke as all her anxiety dissolved. 'I promise. Luke—I shall always remember what you've just said.'

'Good girl.' He sat down again. 'I know I've just suggested we forget the whole thing,' he said, 'but I would like to ask you this: why are you taking it so calmly?'

'I had time to think about it while I was dressing. I

realise the temptation you had—and you were, like me, affected by the wine, you know, so that has something to do with it. But mainly it was the situation—a man and a woman late at night, together.' She shrugged her shoulders. 'It could have happened to any two people who were together like that. If I'd been someone else, you'd still have tried to make love to her, wouldn't you?'

A long, tense silence followed before Luke spoke. 'So your attitude's a philosophical one? You just look upon yourself as a woman—any woman—whom I found attractive and wanted to make love to?'

There was an edge of bitterness to his voice which brought her eyes swiftly to his. She was puzzled again, and this time floundering to grasp something even while not knowing what it was. 'Yes, that's how I see it,' she answered after a pause. 'The situation became more intimate by my attitude; I was unhappy. I kissed you and, because we'd both had a little too much wine, the inevitable happened.'

'The inevitable,' he murmured. He looked at her. 'You believe that whatever female happened to be with me, I'd have acted exactly as I did?'

She nodded. 'That's what I'm saying, Luke—' She stopped, troubled. 'I hope I haven't offended you by this perfectly logical explanation?'

'Logical and clinical—' Suddenly he had to laugh and a weight fell from her mind. 'You haven't offended me, Chris,' he added and dug his spoon into his grapefruit again.

'You asked me why I was taking it so calmly and I have given you the explanation. But as I admitted just now, I was troubled as to your opinion of me. When first I woke up I was filled with embarrassment and shame.' She was staring straightly at him with no sign of embarrassment about her now. Her violet eyes were wide and limpid and innocent. 'You've reassured me, Luke, and I thank you for it. I could never be happy if your opinion of me changed. I need you always and you know it.' So serious her expression as the frank admission was made.

Luke seemed to give a little sigh but all he said was, 'You're not eating, Chris.' He watched as she took up her spoon. 'From this moment we shall forget it ever happened, all right?'

'All right!' She was happy again—well, as happy as she could be under the circumstances, she told herself. Strange, she was thinking, but the first thought that should have entered her mind this morning should have been about Steve, and his new wife . . . and the night they had spent together. Her heart should have been achingly affected by what her brain was imagining. But it was Luke's face that came instantly before her. Luke whose opinion of her mattered so much. Yes, it was Luke who occupied her thoughts to the exclusion of everyone else . . . including Steve, the man she loved.

The plane made a smooth landing on Grand Bahama Island and they were in the car when Christine turned impulsively to her companion. 'Thank you for bringing me, Luke. I had to get away from Pirates' Cay for a while.'

'It'll all have settled by the time you get back,' he assured her.

'Everyone kept on talking about the wedding. Wherever I went I was having to listen to comments on the lovely bride and handsome bridegroom.'

'This crush you have on Steve,' began Luke when she interrupted him.

'It's not a crush, Luke, not calf love, as you insist. I love him and shall never marry anyone else.'

'That's how you feel now but in another six months you'll have forgotten him. It's a blessing that he and Greta won't be living on Pirates' Cay.'

'I wonder how long it will be before they come back for a holiday?'

'You want them to?'

'Yes and no.' She sighed. She was remembering Steve's kiss and his saying that if he hadn't been marrying Greta, then he'd have waited for her. Her heart had cried that he'd have had no need to wait; she would have been his for the taking. 'I suppose I ought not to want Steve to come back yet. . . .'

An impatient sigh escaped her companion which made her subside into silence. It wasn't difficult, for she had plenty to think about. The days following the wedding when, as she had told Luke, she'd been forced to listen to the comments on the wedding, and especially the lovely bride who had been lucky enough to win a man like Steve for a husband. Steve was popular and rich; he was handsome in his rugged sort of way. The moment she set eyes on him Christine had told herself that she preferred the rugged type even though she was willing to admit that Luke's angular, aristocratic features were inordinately attractive in spite of their forbidding aspect at times.

49

Would she get over Steve, as Luke maintained she must? He was older than Luke by eight years, which meant he was seventeen years older than she. . . .

'Perhaps he would have been too old for me—' She stopped, not having intended to speak her thoughts aloud.

'You're telling yourself that—by way of compensation?' The cool mockery of his tone brought a hint of colour to her cheeks.

'I'm sorry— But I can't understand why you are angered every time I speak of Steve.'

'I'm more impatient than angry. Forget him! He wasn't for you, so be big enough to accept that! Now, for heaven's sake let me hear no more about *your sister's husband*!'

'Oh!' She felt the tears stinging her eyes. 'You're cruel to put it like that—stressing the fact that he's married to Greta!'

'I could shake you,' was his unexpected rejoinder spoken in a very soft voice. 'Grow up, Christine!'

'You've said I have grown up!'

'Then I was mistaken. You act like a moonstruck schoolgirl!'

Again she fell silent, her mouth quivering. These changes in Luke of late—what was the explanation for them? He had always been so patient and understanding and she would have expected sympathy in her present affliction and heartbreak, but instead he was hard with her, and almost callous just now in emphasising the fact that Steve was now totally out of her reach.

'I wish I'd stayed at home and started that job,' she snapped.

'Your father didn't want you to have the job.'

'Nor did you, it would seem.'

'Christine, I have no say in whether or not you take a job!'

Christine again . . . He only used that when he was angry with her . . . so very seldom. . . .

She swallowed the hurt in her throat and said spiritedly, 'As it's such a bad start to this visit, I think perhaps I shall go home!'

'Very well! Do you want to be taken back to the airport?' It was his own car they were in, as he kept a car permanently at the hotel in Freeport. 'Shall I tell Joseph to turn around?'

Staggered, she could only stare at him, aware of the rigid set of his profile, the tightness of his mouth. She was lately seeing a man she had never seen before. Was this the man on whose shoulder she had so often wept and been comforted each time? Luke, her support through all the years when in moments of craving for affection she had not been able to find it at Cassia Lodge. True, her adoptive father did care for her, but he cared for his business more. And there was no affection to be had either from her mother or from Greta. No, always it had been to Luke she had turned, and never had he failed her . . . never until now, and the only explanation that occurred to her was that he had become tired of the relationship now that he was getting older. Changes. How she hated them!

'I've asked you a question,' she heard him say crisply. 'Do you want Joseph to turn around?'

'N-no,' she murmured on a tiny sob. 'You know very well I—I don't.'

Luke seemed not to have the patience to reply and

the rest of the journey passed in silence. On entering the hotel, however, Christine could not suppress the impulsive exclamation that came to her lips. 'It's beautiful, Luke! All these chandeliers! How they sparkle, and this crystal cascade—!' She pointed to the imitation waterfall in the centre of the massive lobby. 'It looks so real!'

'The glass came from Venice,' he told her, a chill edge to his tone.

'It was here when you bought the hotel?'

Luke nodded and strode towards the lift, Christine following with the heaviness descending on her heart again. However, once in his private suite Luke soon became his own amicable self.

'I'm sorry, Luke.' Christine's manner was contrite. 'I won't be stupid and childish again. It—hurts when you're angry with me.'

He shook his head and gave a small sigh. 'Sometimes, Chris, I just don't know what to do with you.'

'We're both getting older, and changes are coming. I don't like them but realise they're inevitable.'

He was by the window, looking down at the pool around which a number of guests were sunbathing, attired only in the briefest covering. Brown bodies lazily taking on more and more sun. In the pool itself the swimmers enjoyed the warmth and the pleasure of the bar which Luke had recently had put into the centre of the swimming pool. It was something different which the hotel guests seemed to find intriguing.

Luke turned on Christine's words and a wry smile touched the fine outline of his mouth. 'Yes, we're getting older,' he agreed, 'and the changes come.'

'What shall I ever do without you when eventually you cast me off?' Not words she had really meant to utter but she was keenly interested in his response. Her lovely eyes were wide and appealing, her fingers nervously plucking at one another.

'What makes you suppose I shall ever cast you off?'

'I'm beginning to bore you,' she asserted, trying to read his expression, but his face had taken on a masklike quality—a calculated act, she felt sure, in order to keep her in ignorance of his feelings, and her heart sank a little as she was sure he was mentally agreeing with what she had said.

'I shan't cast you off,' was all he said, glancing to the door as a porter brought in their luggage.

'Is that meant to be reassuring?' she wanted to know after the man had left again.

'I hope it is reassuring, Chris.' Serious the tone and the honest look as his eyes met hers.

Nevertheless, she was impelled to say, her mind having winged to what Greta had told her about Luke having a glamourous girlfriend, 'You'll marry, Luke, and then I shall be without you, for I'm sure your wife won't want you to be bothering about me and my troubles.'

'Troubles,' he repeated and was suddenly amused. 'At your age, child, the only troubles are those of the tender years, but, sadly, you don't realise that, and if you did you wouldn't accept it.'

'The tender years . . .' She looked questioningly at him. 'You mean the teens?'

'Yes, I expect the teens is what I mean.'

'They should be the best years of a girl's life.'

'Usually they are—'

'For most girls, yes, but for me—' She stopped as a sense of ingratitude assailed her.

'But you feel you've missed a good deal? I suppose you have,' he added after a small pause, 'and yet there are a great number of girls who would envy you the life you live.'

The hint of censure did not escape her and she was swift to respond, 'I know that you are right, Luke. I'm ungrateful and selfish because I sometimes dwell on what might have been had my parents lived. We were so happy and there was love in our home.'

Luke came towards her, and as had happened so often in the past she was finding a resting place for her head against his breast.

'I don't deserve you,' she admitted. 'It will be my own fault if you tire of all this.' He made no answer, but just continued to stroke her soft, shining hair. 'You will marry,' she insisted. 'And this will become a memory.'

'I'm not thinking of marrying yet awhile, so we can let that problem slide.'

'But one day you *must* marry.'

'Perhaps.' He drew her away and looked into her eyes. 'Who knows?'

Christine lowered her head, profoundly aware of those inexplicable vibrations again, and a hollowness within her this time, too. Luke married . . . Until now she had treated the possibility lightly, without troubling to form pictures or think deeply about it. But now the picture had assumed a clarity which brought it right home to her. All his love and affection would be lavished on his wife, while she, Christine, would become so unimportant that she would be forgotten altogether—well, perhaps not altogether because they would see each other, both living on Pirates' Cay. Or would Luke decide to live here, on Grand Bahama, or perhaps in Nassau? Christine's eyes were bleak as she looked up, forced to do so by a lean brown hand beneath her chin.

'Lord, Chris, what's wrong?' he demanded with a frown of concern.

'I was imagining you married—Oh, Luke, whatever shall I do without you?' The words came out on a strangled cry, but instead of sympathy Christine received a thorough shaking.

'Stop it!' thundered Luke, ready to shake her again. 'It was childishness before and now it's self-pity. If I marry, *then* is the time for you to wonder! And now—go and unpack! Your room's over there, the door on the left!'

'Wonder?' she was saying to herself as she turned to obey him. 'What an odd word to use. Wonder . . .'

Why, thought Christine, hadn't she expected something like this? After all, Miami was little more than a stone's throw across the Atlantic Ocean and so it was easy for Luke's girl friend to come over. Probably she had been in the habit of doing so each time Luke was on the island of Grand Bahama. Greta had said that Clarice was glamourous; she had beauty as well, and poise and a certain amount of grace. She had arrived within twenty-four hours of their own arrival and now, as she stood on the balcony of her bedroom, Christine could see them in the pool, swimming close, laughing comrades who obviously found pleasure in each other's company.

She turned, having come up to change because Luke had insisted she go into the pool, but she felt the invitation to be nothing more than courtesy . . . or he might be feeling sorry for her— No, not that any more, she decided. Luke was still impatient if she only mentioned Steve's name.

She didn't change, but she went down to the pool patio and took possession of a lounger. She was in bright green shorts and a white cotton sun top which was tight and scanty so that it revealed her tanned arms and throat and most of her back. She noticed the attention of a young man she had seen watching her before. He smiled as their eyes met and she smiled back. A moment later his chair was alongside her lounger and he was introducing himself.

'Kevin Peyton,' she repeated. 'I'm Christine Mead.'

'Happy to make your acquaintance. I've been noticing you for the past two days. You're with the couple in there, aren't you?'

She nodded, her eyes going to Luke's bronzed body as he swam away to the other side of the pool. *With that couple* . . . The odd one out, gooseberry. She bit her lip, conscious of a new and disturbing emotion she could not have described had her life depended on it.

'Are you on holiday?' she asked presently.

'In a way. But I really came for an interview for a job as assistant manager at the Pioneer Hotel. I thought I'd come a few days beforehand and enjoy a bit of sun.'

'You're American. They don't usually have foreigners in a job a Bahamian can do—at least, that's the rule applying on Pirates' Cay, where I come from.'

'You live in the Bahamas, then?'

'Yes, I do.'

'Lucky! So you don't hold out much hope of my getting the job?'

'Hope?' She shrugged her shoulders, thinking it rather strange that he should bring her opinion into it. She didn't care one way or the other, but of course she was too polite to say so. 'I might be wrong,' she eventually said, 'but they usually think of their own people first.'

'I want to be optimistic, though. I feel the hotel owner wouldn't have asked me to come if there's no chance.'

'I agree, so it might be that the owner can pull some strings.' Her eyes strayed to the pool again; Luke and Clarice were sitting on the side, very close together.

'It's not much fun being on my own here.' He turned towards her, an expectant look in his deep-set grey eyes. 'I know you're with that couple, but would you break away this evening and dine with me?'

'No, I couldn't do that.'

'Why? I daresay they'd welcome a chance to be alone—' He stopped, appearing almost comical in his dismay. 'I must be a fool to have said a thing like that. I'm so sorry—I mean, if they—'

'It's all right,' she broke in coldly. 'There's no need to apologise.' She reached for the book she had brought down with her and dropped on the ground. 'If you'll excuse me?' She rose and walked away but he followed, much to her annoyance.

'I really am sorry, Christine—'

'Don't call me Christine,' she snapped. 'And kindly leave me alone.'

But he still followed on her brisk pace and in the lobby she turned. He was looking extremely crestfallen and contrite. Christine felt sorry for him even though she was still angry. She supposed it was humiliation which was really affecting her, making her feel so uncomfortable. Did Luke want to be alone with Clarice? No need to ask if the girl wanted him all to herself, for although she had been friendly towards Christine, there was an underlying resentment of her presence which Christine was quick to sense. She wondered what explanation Luke had given to the girl. Christine hadn't asked him but she would, at the first opportunity.

'Say you forgive me,' Kevin was saying in a humble tone.

'Forget it,' she said and managed a smile. 'We can all be guilty of a slip of the tongue.'

Half an hour later Luke was asking why she hadn't come into the pool. He and Christine were in the luxurious sitting room of the suite; the window was wide open with only the insect netting between them and the flower-draped balcony which looked out over the marina.

'I didn't want to—to intrude.'

Luke, who was now in buff-coloured slacks and a casual overshirt, opened his eyes wide at her sullen tone. 'That's an odd word to use, isn't it?'

'Clarice and you—' She broke off and began again. 'I'm not happy at playing gooseberry.'

An exasperated sigh issued from his lips. 'What the devil's got into you now?' he demanded, coming close to tower above her. 'You came here with me and it's my duty to see you enjoy yourself!'

'Duty?' She lifted her eyes, saw him frown as he guessed she was close to tears. 'Why should you feel you have a duty towards me? It's natural that you want to be with Clarice, and if I'd known she was coming here, then I'd have stayed at home. You should have told me she was going to be with us.'

'I didn't know she was coming here,' he snapped. 'I phoned her when we arrived and it was a mistake—' Glowering at Christine as if it were her fault he had made the slip, he swung away abruptly to the other side of the room but turned to face her. 'She decided to come over—'

'Without asking you?' interrupted Christine.

'Yes—she didn't know I had anyone with me.'

'I see.'

'You don't see at all! However, it doesn't matter. That you resent her is plain but there's nothing I can do about it. She's here and you can get used to the idea. She's been friendly towards you and she's mentioned what a charming child you are, so why this antagonism?'

'She called me a child?' No answer from Luke, who merely threw her an impatient glance. 'I'm not antagonistic,' she went on to deny. 'Nor do I resent her being here. What troubles me is the knowledge that you and she would prefer to be alone. It's a pity I came with you,' she added. Then, stung to a retort by his sudden gleam of contempt, she threw in for good measure, 'I'm sorry I've cramped your style!'

Luke gritted his teeth. 'You have *not* cramped my style! If I want to be alone with Clarice all I've to do is pack you off back to Pirates' Cay on the next flight out!'

Christine's lips quivered. 'Luke . . . this is the first time you and I have quarrelled.'

His eyes were almost hostile. 'It'll not be the last if you go on like this. It's the crush you have on Steve, and the sooner you make up your mind to forget him the sooner you'll be a nice person again. As it is— you're peevish and truculent and bad-tempered—' He wagged a finger at her threateningly. 'You've said you wished I were your guardian, your adoptive father. Well, you can thank your lucky stars that I'm not, because if I were I'd throw you over my knee and give you the spanking you deserve.'

She stared, the hot blood surging into her cheeks. 'Why, you—!' she began, then broke off as the door opened.

'I hope I'm not interrupting anything,' came the voice of Clarice at its sweetest as she sailed into the room. 'But I forgot to tell you, Luke, darling, that I've a hair appointment in ten minutes and so I could be a little late for lunch. Shall we make it for a quarter past one instead of one o'clock?' While speaking to Luke her eyes were nevertheless flickering to the angry, flushed face of the girl who was standing in the middle of the room, her fists tightly clenched at her sides.

'That'll be all right, Clarice; we'll be in the lounge having an apéritif.'

'I shan't be having lunch,' from Christine tautly. 'I'm not hungry,' and with that she turned away, swiftly, because her eyes were brimming with tears of self-pity and anger.

She bumped into Kevin as she came out of the lift. 'Oh—hello,' she greeted him. 'Er—about this evening. Is the invitation still on?'

'Of course,' he replied eagerly. 'You'll have dinner with me?'

'I'd love to.' She paused fractionally. 'Lunch—I'm on my own for the rest of the day.'

She was being horrid and she knew it. For it was not Luke's fault that Clarice was here, but as long as she was he had to be gracious to her. What did she, Christine, expect him to do—tell the girl to go off and entertain herself, because he had a young friend with him? I'm rotten, decided Christine and tears rolled unchecked down her cheeks, tears of regret that she could even think of being so hateful with her dearest Luke.

Chapter Four

Luke's face was set in rigid lines and there was a wrathful thrust to his voice as he said, 'You'll have dinner with Clarice and me— No more arguments!' he added when Christine opened her mouth to interrupt. 'You're here in my care; your father would never have allowed you to come on your own—'

'I *am* eighteen!' she cried indignantly.

'And please don't interrupt me,' rasped Luke, sending her a glowering glance. 'Your father put you in my care and he'll expect me to look after you. There'll be no dining out for you with this man you've picked up at the poolside.'

'I didn't pick him up!'

'No? Then he picked you up. What's the difference? The argument's ended,' he said repressively and walked with unhurried steps to the cocktail cabinet to pour himself a drink.

'Do you suppose I shall let Kevin down just because you are adopting this dictatorial manner with me?' Defiance edged her tone but in her heart there was pain. What was happening to her and Luke these days? He had never been like this with her before . . . but, she was quick to own, neither had she been like this with him. She had always treated him with respect, remembering that he was older; she had always accepted his advice, admitting he was wiser; she had always allowed herself to be bent to his will, because of his mastery—gentle mastery it was true, but his word was to be obeyed for all that. But now . . . She was defiant, but why? It was a question she was unable to answer and she felt ashamed because the more she dwelt on her behaviour the less excuse she could find for it. Luke had poured the drink and was holding the glass in his long fingers, twirling it as if to see the oily surface catch the light.

'Did you want a drink?' he asked.

'You've ignored my question, Luke.'

'I've said my last concerning the matter of whom you are dining with. You'll do as I say, Chris, and forget this date you have made.'

She bit her lip, aware of his austere withdrawal as he sat down and put the glass on a side table close to his chair. He seemed no longer interested in her and she wondered if he had forgotten he'd asked her to have a drink.

'I feel the odd one out,' she said at last. 'Surely you want to be with your girl friend—alone with her, I mean?'

'I'm quite happy with the situation as it is.' He looked at her over the rim of his glass he had now picked up. 'And if *I'm* not complaining, then why should you?'

'It's not a complaint,' she denied. 'I just feel—well, out of it.'

'Rubbish!' His anger was dissolving but impatience took its place. 'It's this thing about Steve—'

'It has nothing to do with Steve,' she said. 'It's me—the way I feel.' She swung around, expecting to see Clarice come into the room but the door was swinging open on its own. She moved to close it, murmuring, 'I thought it was Clarice.'

'She'll not be coming here; she's to meet us in the lounge in half an hour.'

'She's not coming here—why?'

'Because I haven't invited her.'

'Does she need to be invited, then?'

'Of course, seeing that this is my private sitting room.'

Christine frowned in puzzlement. 'But if she's your girl friend, then she'll feel she has a right to come and go, surely?'

'Just how serious do you imagine my friendship is with Clarice?' he asked, leaning forward to lift his glass again.

'It isn't serious?' A leaden weight was lifting with every second that passed.

'Not at the moment,' answered Luke calmly, but after a slight pause he added, fixing his eyes on hers with an inscrutable expression, 'For the future—who knows?'

'It could become serious, you mean?'

'Perhaps.' Abruptly he changed the subject. 'I think you had better phone this Kevin and tell him you've changed your mind. While you do that I'll pour you a drink. Martini?'

'Yes, please.' She hesitated, feeling sorry for Kevin. 'I—'

'Use this phone,' he said, flicking a hand towards it.

'There's no need for you to go to your bedroom. It isn't as if you've anything private to say.'

She sent him a speaking glance and saw his mouth curve in amusement. With a sigh of resignation she did as he told her. Kevin was disappointed and would have plied her with questions but she said on a note of finality, 'I'm very sorry, Kevin, but it isn't possible. I ought not to have made the date. Good-bye.'

'Your drink, dear,' Luke said as she turned.

Dear . . .

'We're friends again, Luke?' The tremor in her voice brought a slight frown to his brow.

'Is it so important to you that we be friends?' he asked and her eyes widened to their fullest extent.

'You know it is. I've said so many times that I need you, Luke,' she added seriously, 'you're all I've got.'

'What about your father?'

'He loves me, yes, but he's always occupied with business—well, almost always.' There was a note of despondency in her voice but she forced a smile to her lips. 'No, Luke, it is you I depend on; you're my one sure prop and if I lost you . . .' Her voice trailed to silence as she thought of Clarice and the possibility of his eventually marrying her. But it would not be yet—not for a long while, she thought, judging by his attitude and the way he had spoken about her.

'You're a strange girl,' murmured Luke with a sigh. 'I once believed I understood you but now—' He shook his head and added ruefully, 'You baffle me, Chris, and yet I know that you don't mean to be perverse.' The tender years, he mused as he sipped his drink, years of bewilderment, uncertainty and insecurity. He ought not to lose his patience with her. 'Come here,' he said gently as he got to his feet.

Startled, she stared at him, but then rose and went to him, her slender frame delightfully clad in a long evening dress of clinging satin that accentuated its youthful curves.

'What do you want?' she asked.

'Just to kiss you and let you know we're friends again.'

Tears filled her eyes as emotion flooded over her. 'Oh, Luke—you're so—so kind to me!'

'Not always, I'm afraid. I'm only human, though, and I'm a man. Those are the excuses I offer for sometimes losing my temper with you.'

He had reached her; he took her arms in his hands and she tilted her face, vitally conscious of increased heartbeats and racing pulse.

'What did your words mean?' she asked before his lips touched hers. He kissed her gently and held her close. Her hands came up to meet at the back of his neck.

'You will understand them one day, my dear,' he answered, holding her at arm's length.

'You say I baffle you, Luke, but you often baffle me by these cryptic remarks.'

He made no comment but bent his head and kissed her again.

She said, rather hesitantly, 'We've almost half an hour to ourselves before we go down to dinner.'

He nodded and went back to his chair. 'Clarice is leaving tomorrow afternoon,' he said casually.

'She is?' Christine's eyes were glowing. 'But we are staying for another four days, aren't we?'

He gave a low laugh and said, 'How very transparent you are, Chris. However, it's most gratifying to know you like being alone with me.'

'You've always known it,' she retorted.

'I shall have to leave you all day on Thursday.' Luke said, abruptly changing the subject. 'I've to fly over to Florida on business.'

'I'll find something to do,' she said. 'What time shall you be back?'

'In plenty of time for dinner.'

'I like this island, Luke. I wouldn't mind living here.'

'You wouldn't?' His eyes became veiled. 'It's a lot bigger than what you've been used to.'

'I know—and I must admit that small islands are nice to live on, but there's something very attractive about Grand Bahama, don't you think?'

'I certainly do or otherwise I'd not have bought this hotel. I'm also considering buying a house here, close to the water, so that I can bring the yacht over.'

'You'd live here?'

'One day perhaps.'

'When you're married?'

'Must you keep on about marriage?' he asked in some amusement. 'You seem to have it on the brain.'

'You're twenty-seven and that's quite old. Most men are married by that age.'

'Old, you think?'

'No, I shouldn't have said that. Twenty-seven's a rather wonderful age for a man.'

'Tell me,' he said, 'do you look upon me as a lot older than you?'

She pondered this a moment before answering. Luke, watching her, saw the pensive expression in her lovely eyes, the pursing of her full, generous mouth. His eyes moved to the delicate blue tracery of veins in her temple, to the silken mantle of her hair, then down to the alluring swell of her throat and the slope of her shoulders.

'No, not always,' she replied at last. 'Sometimes, when you scold me or domineer over me, then you seem much older, but at times like now you seem much younger.'

His mouth curved in amusement. 'Do I really domineer over you, my dear?'

"You know you do!'

"And I scold you?'

She had to laugh. 'What is this? A cross-examination?'

'A personal investigation.'

She laughed again. 'We're back to old times,' she said, 'when we were like brother and sister. . . .' Her voice faltered to a stop and her long curling lashes swept down, hiding her expression and at the same time throwing delectable shadows onto her cheeks.

'What is it?' he enquired gently. 'Why did you stop?'

'I don't know—' She brought her head up. 'We're not really like brother and sister, are we, Luke?'

He shook his head. 'Nor like guardian and ward.'

'Like very good friends, then?'

His gaze was keen and searching. 'You want us to be very good friends?'

She frowned at him in puzzlement. 'Haven't we always been good friends—except for the few occasions, lately, when we've seemed to disagree?'

He said, after a long unfathomable pause, 'Let's

change the subject, shall we? I'm free all day Wednesday, so what would you like to do?'

'I want to explore the island, and I want to do some more shopping in the International Market; it fascinates me with all those shops from all parts of the world. I bought some jade from the Chinese shop and some hand embroidery from the Greek shop. I bought the jade for Uncle Arthur—' She stopped and sighed. 'Why do I keep calling him Uncle lately when I used always to call him Father?'

Luke shook his head. 'That's a question only you yourself can answer,' he said, but he had recently guessed that she was becoming more and more insecure as regards her home life and he firmly believed it was owing to Loreen and the amount of time she spent away from home. Arthur was away, too, during the whole of the daytime, living for his business. This meant that Christine, instead of drawing closer to her adoptive parents as she grew older, was in fact finding herself on the edge of an ever-widening chasm which she knew she could never bridge. Luke was troubled about her; aware of her volatile nature, he feared she might one day tell him she wanted to leave home.

And where would she go?

'I'd rather look upon him as my father,' she was saying seriously, 'but, somehow, he seems nowadays to be more like an uncle . . . sort of distant. Perhaps,' she went on as if talking to herself, 'it's because he's away from home so much, or it could be that it is I who am changing.'

Luke glanced at his watch. 'We'd better be going down, Chris.' Rising, he moved to pull her up beside him. 'Arthur needs you,' he stated, 'so don't do anything to upset him. Promise me,' he added and now his tone had an imperious edge to it, matching the sudden stern, masterful expression in his eyes.

'I promise, Luke—' She lifted her face, closed her eyes as he bent to touch her wide forehead with his lips. 'Why should you want to extract a promise like that from me? You know I'd never hurt my—uncle. I owe him far too much.'

Conscious of what she owed . . . But would she always feel like this? He stared down into the young and lovely face, slid his fingers through that unruly half fringe and said, 'Just remember the promise, dear; that's something I am asking you and the whys and wherefores are not important.'

'Cryptic remarks again,' she said, but with a smile. 'I shall remember the promise I made you, Luke, so please do not doubt me.' She was puzzled as to why he had insisted on having such a promise from her, for surely he knew she would never dream of deliberately hurting the man who had given her a home and a certain amount of affection.

Clarice was tapping her foot impatiently when, glancing up, she saw Luke and Christine approaching the table at which she sat with her apéritif. There was a glint in her eyes as she swept them over Christine's figure with an almost contemptuous expression. Her face was faintly flushed, and although it added to its beauty it also gave evidence of an anger within her.

'I've been waiting for over a quarter of an hour,' she told Luke in a quivering tone which she was plainly having difficulty in controlling. Christine felt sure that fury was vibrating deep within the girl and she found herself feeling sorry for her. She was Luke's girl friend and here he was, with someone else, surveying Clarice with an almost impersonal amicability he might have displayed to someone who was little more than a casual acquaintance. Still, mused Christine as she and Luke sat down for a moment, Clarice *had* come here uninvited, after Luke's phone call, and she hadn't wasted much time, either. Christine had asked Luke how he had explained her presence to Clarice and his answer had been that he did not explain anything unless he wished to do so.

'But she must have wondered who I am,' persisted Christine.

'She knows about you,' he replied briefly.

'Didn't she wonder why you should be bringing me here with you on this business trip?'

'She did ask the reason. I merely said you sometimes do come with me on these trips.'

'That wasn't a very satisfactory answer, surely?'

'It sufficed. Clarice knows better than to make an issue of anything with me.'

Christine had looked at him, at the firm line of the jaw, the implacable set of the mouth, and surmised that if Clarice knew anything about him at all she would know how to read an expression like that. Christine certainly did.

'You've been waiting a quarter of an hour,' Luke was saying to Clarice, his words a response to her complaint. 'But we arranged to meet here at eight o'clock and it's still two minutes to.'

Clarice lowered her lashes, hiding her expression. 'I came early,' she said.

'Have you looked at the menu?'

Was that a snub? wondered Christine. Luke had a rather subtle way of making you feel small by changing the subject like that.

'Yes, I don't want much—just a salad and some cold meats.'

Luke shrugged; the dinner was a strain on Christine and she felt sure it was to Clarice also, but Luke? He appeared to enjoy the meal and he talked when he felt the silence was becoming too strained. It was impossible to know whether he had sensed the dislike the two girls felt for one another.

After dinner Luke had to leave them for an hour as he had an appointment with the manager of the hotel, so to her dismay Christine found herself alone with Luke's friend, a situation she had hitherto managed to avoid.

'Shall we go for a stroll along the beach?' she suggested, hoping that Clarice would oblige by saying she would rather go straight up to her bedroom. But she said yes, she would like a walk along the beach.

They had not gone far when Clarice said, nothing in her voice to betray her dislike, 'You're lucky to be staying on for another few days. I wish I was.'

'You couldn't manage it, you said?'

'I have a job. I took these few days of my annual holiday when Luke phoned to say he was here. I'd no idea he had anyone with him.' She turned to look at Christine. 'He thinks a lot of you. I feel he regards you as a daughter.'

'He intimated that?'

'In a way,' answered Clarice, smiling. 'He's talked about you at various times and that's the impression I had—that he has a fatherly feeling for you.'

'He's always been someone I could lean on. . . .' Christine let her voice fade to silence, regretting the confidence.

'You needed someone to lean upon, then?'

'Everyone needs a friend,' was Christine's evasive answer. 'Luke can always be relied on to be my very good friend.'

'And that's how you feel about him . . . nothing more?'

'More?' Suddenly she was living again that intimate experience when Luke had awakened—if only temporarily—emotions she had never known before.

'Well, he is more than a little attractive, isn't he—even with that scar which sometimes—to me anyway—is scarcely noticeable.'

'Nor is it noticeable to me.' A small pause and then, 'How long have you known Luke?'

'Not long—just over four months.'

'I've known him for seven years.' Christine didn't know why she said that, unless she was being faintly patronising towards the other girl.

'Long enough for the friendship to have gone rather stale,' commented Clarice with a laugh that seemed to have no humour.

'Our friendship will never grow stale.' Christine was bored with the girl and would have done anything to be able to bid her good-bye and walk away. She wanted to be alone, and as the beach was deserted that would have been possible had it not been for Clarice. A long curving stretch of talcum-soft sand, with trees backing the shore to provide welcome shade during the daytime from the intensely bright rays of the sun.

'You sound very optimistic,' commented Clarice, stooping to slip off her shoes.

'I feel optimistic.'

'What about when Luke marries?' Slow the words and with an undercurrent that caused Christine's blood to feel cold all at once. Yet why should she have any fears? Luke's manner with Clarice was surely proof enough that he wasn't at present contemplating marriage. Moreover, he had said quite firmly that he wasn't.

'I think that we might still be very good friends,' she said at last.

'Luke's wife might not like it. Have you thought of that?'

'Yes, of course.' Christine injected a chill note into her voice because she had no wish to continue this sort of conversation. She felt that the other girl was playing with her.

'If it were I, then I'd object. Strongly.' Clarice straightened up and they walked on, Clarice swinging her shoes by their straps. Christine looked at her with a sidelong glance. A pretty dress of flowered cotton, low in the neck and without sleeves. A white kid bag over her shoulder, a diamanté comb in her chestnut hair. Most attractive, Christine grudgingly owned. It was not beyond the bounds of possibility that Luke would one day fall for all these feminine attractions—yes, no matter how perfunctory his interest at the present time. A calculated technique on Clarice's part, and given sufficient time and ample opportunity she could succeed in getting what she wanted, which was undoubtedly to win Luke for her husband.

'It could be a long time before Luke marries.' Christine spoke at last, remembering what he had said concerning the possibility of his marrying—one day.

'You think so?' There was the suspicion of a sneer about Clarice's mouth when perceived in profile. 'Perhaps the wish is father to the thought,' she quoted.

'It's unprofitable to discuss it,' said Christine coolly, 'since it's impossible to predict just how long it will be before he gets married.'

'You're not in love with him?'

The forthright question took Christine aback but she answered without hesitation, 'Of course not!'

Clarice made no comment, and after they had walked a little while longer over the moonlit sands Christine suggested they turn back. 'Luke might finish the interview early,' she added, 'and so I feel we ought to get back so as not to keep him waiting.'

Chapter Five

Arthur Mead was sitting alone at the breakfast table when Christine went along to join him. He hadn't been too well lately and it seemed wrong for his wife to go away on holiday at this particular time.

'Are you feeling any better?' asked Christine anxiously as she sat down opposite to him.

'A little.' He smiled at her and commented on her dress, saying it was pretty and that blue suited her. 'Is it new?' he added. 'I don't remember seeing it before.'

'It isn't new. I've had it ages.'

'I've had a letter from Greta,' he said a short while later. 'She and Steve are coming over for a visit next week.'

'They . . . are?' Steve—to see him again! 'It's just six months since they were married,' she recollected.

'Seems much less than that.'

'How long will they be staying?' Christine felt her pulses racing, her heart beating much too quickly. Steve . . .

'Greta didn't say. But it'll be for a while, I think, judging by the gist of her letter.'

'Did you write to tell her you weren't well? Is that why they're coming?'

He shook his head. 'I haven't written for over a month.'

'Did she say what day they'd be over?' Christine helped herself to toast and marmalade while Arthur poured her a cup of coffee.

'She thinks Thursday, but she'll give me a ring before then.'

Christine was suddenly puzzled by his manner and she was impelled to ask, 'Is something wrong, Father?'

He was frowning, but at her words his brow cleared. 'No—er—what makes you ask that?' He was not looking at her and her puzzlement increased.

'I don't really know. You seem—worried, sort of.'

He shrugged his shoulders and lapsed into silence. After a while Christine asked if Loreen would be home for Greta's visit.

'I've no idea. I should think she'll be back by then.' His tone was flat, expressionless. 'She's been away ten days already,' he added as if he had been mentally reckoning up the time.

'Are you going to the office today?' Christine felt the need of company and Luke was in Nassau. Her thoughts were all on Steve and would remain so unless she had some diversion. 'Let's go to the beach, just you and me, and have lunch at the Fisherman's Reef—they do those delicious small sea fish marinated in lime juice, remember? They garnish them with herbs and garlic butter.' Her voice was low and persuasive, her big violet eyes anxiously darkened by her plea. 'We could swim first, then soak up the sun, have lunch, and afterwards have a little drive round the island. I want to buy some plants from Hydraflora—small palms and allamandas for my balcony.' Eager and encouraging, she forgot her manners and leant her elbows on the table, cupping her chin in her hands. 'You work too hard, love, so please take today off.'

'It would be nice,' he agreed, but—' To her disappointment he shook his head. 'I've a lot to do—some other time, dear.'

Her body sagged. She wished she had insisted on taking the job offered her. Of late she had known a strange restlessness and on a couple of occasions she could almost have run away, lost herself in some place right away from Cassia Lodge. Only Luke held her, she realised, and the promise she had made him. Luke, who was, as always, her prop and her haven. She had asked him recently how his affair with Clarice was progressing and had received the kind of noncommittal reply that had effectively discouraged any further enquiries on her part.

'I ought to get a job,' she said with a sigh. 'This hanging around isn't healthy.'

'Healthy?' with a lift of his bushy grey eyebrows. 'That's an odd word to use, isn't it?'

'One gets morbid. I like being alone sometimes—I think everybody does—but since Greta went, and with Mother . . .' She tailed off but Arthur finished for her, 'Being away from home so much you feel lonely.'

She nodded her head. 'If I had a job, it would at least fill my days.'

'You do a good job here—supervising the servants, planning the meals. You should be glad there's no need for you to go out to work.'

'I'd have company.'

'You've friends, haven't you?'

'Some are married and others have jobs.' She knew she sounded discontented but her voice was only a reflection of her thoughts. This life was becoming more and more boring; she felt as if she were drifting and sometimes the future frightened her.

'What about boyfriends? Other girls seem to have several at one and the same time.' Amusement edged Arthur's voice as he added, 'Greta had dozens before finally settling for Steve. . . .' His voice trailed unexpectedly, his humour being replaced by a frown and a tightening of his lips as if he were suppressing a sigh. He glanced at his watch, then rose from the table. 'I must be off. Have a nice day.' He was gone; she sat there looking at the piece of pawpaw he had left, and the roll and butter on his side plate. His cup was half filled with coffee.

Christine felt a tremor of acute uneasiness affecting her nerves. Her father was changing in some indefinable way and she felt he had more on his mind than he would have her know.

Listening, she heard the front door close and, a moment or two later, the engine of his car. It was only a short journey to his office and yet he always used the car. Ten minutes' walk a day would do him good, she thought.

Later, she decided to phone Luke. It would use up a few minutes of this monotonous time she was having to get through. He was pleased to hear her voice but went very quiet after she had said, 'Greta and Steve are coming next week for a visit.'

'Already?' His voice was tight when it reached her after the long pause.

'They've been married six months. It's time they paid their parents a visit. I expect Steve's mum and dad will be glad to see him.'

'And you?' he asked, the cool brevity seeming to double the distance between them.

'I'm looking forward to the visit, naturally.'

'Naturally,' he murmured and then, with a briskness she knew was assumed, 'Look, Chris, I'm exceedingly busy just now so I must ring off. Have a nice day.'

Have a nice day. . . . It was usual for people to say that but how was she to have a nice day, here on her own but for the servants? She replaced the receiver with a sigh, under no illusions as to the reason for Luke's behaviour. She ought not to have mentioned her sister and brother-in-law's coming visit. To talk of Steve to Luke these days was like holding out a red rag to a bull. Luke had no patience to listen, even if she only mentioned Steve casually.

'Forget your sister's husband,' had become familiar to Christine and recently she had refrained from mentioning Steve at all.

Steve's smile seemed a little strained and Christine thought she detected a similar strain in his voice as he greeted her as he and his wife arrived at Cassia Lodge. Christine, having taken special care with what bit of makeup she used, and having washed and set her hair only that morning, looked radiant and beautiful, the attractiveness of her honey-gold skin being enhanced by the white sundress she wore which was very low cut and without sleeves. It was short to reveal the full allure of slender legs, also tanned like the rest of her body. Dainty white sandals and a white ribbon bow in her hair completed the picture which had caused an unexpected narrowing of Luke's eyes when he had called a short while before the arrival of the couple. He had seemed to look at Christine with something akin to contempt but she had no chance of asking him what was wrong because, having called merely to see Arthur, he and the older man had gone immediately to the study where they were at present. So it had fallen to Christine to be the one to greet her sister and Steve, as Loreen was still away on holiday.

'You're looking wonderful,' said Steve, holding out both his hands towards her. Greta had shouldered past Christine and was already in the house. 'You've grown an inch or more since I last saw you.'

She laughed to hide her sudden tension; she had no wish that Steve should ever guess at her feelings for him.

'Not that much,' she denied. 'I don't feel any different. . . .' She was confused, fumbling for words, and her eyes were lowered as she stared at her feet. 'How are you, Steve? Do you like your new house? I'd—l-like to come over sometime and—and see it. . . .' Again she became lost for words. Steve's fingers curled around hers and he bent to kiss her lightly on the cheek.

'It's great to be back and to see you. What have you been doing with yourself?' Tucking her arm through his, he went with her into the house. Greta was in the sitting room by the open window, staring out to the ornamental pond where giant lilies shone pink and white, translucent in the sunshine. Christine's nerves seemed to be springing to the alert as the older girl turned, slowly, as if the effort were too much for her. A baby on the way? A dryness caught at Christine's throat and she swallowed convulsively. Steve's baby . . . But no. Greta's figure was as slender as ever.

'You're looking well.' Christine smiled at her sister but the only response was a swift appraisal by eyes that held an unfathomable expression in their depths.

'So are you.' Greta looked over her shoulder to where Steve was standing, just inside the door. 'Where's Father?' she asked Christine.

'In his study. Shall I tell him you've arrived?'

'I expected him to be at the office.'

'He's not been too well lately.' Christine, still tensed, felt the sudden need for enlightenement. 'Is everything all right, Greta? I mean, you're—well—not very—cheerful.'

A deep silence followed and it was Steve who broke it, merely saying, 'Tell Arthur we're here, Chris. And I'll have a drink if I may?'

Christine flicked a hand. 'You know where it is,' she said, surprised that he should ask at all. He was one of the family, and always previously had helped himself to drinks without asking permission to do so. 'I'll tell Father.'

She knocked lightly on the study door and was invited to enter. Arthur was at his big, leather-topped desk with Luke sitting opposite to him. Christine sent a fleeting glance around the familiar room, liking its maleness, as she liked the maleness of Luke's study. Arthur's taste was rather more flamboyant, though, his having chosen Chinese wallpaper of vivid crimsons and greens and saffrons whereas Luke's walls were plain white, two being lined with bookshelves. One wall took up the massive picture window and the other was covered partly with an exquisite tapestry depicting a scene in a Turkish garden. Arthur's furniture was of light oak, except for the desk which, like Luke's, was a Georgian antique. Luke's furniture was also antique, the small sofa and matching chair being French, exquisitely covered in fine, gold-threaded tapestry.

Both men looked at her as she stood just inside the doorway and she felt the colour rise on noting Luke's expression. He was not pleased with her, but why? It wasn't her fault that Steve was here.

'Greta and Steve are here.' she said and came into the room. 'They've just arrived. Which room have you given them, Father?'

'Me?' He frowned. 'What do I know about rooms? It's your mother's place to be here and see to such things!' Anger lent a glint to his eyes as he went on, 'As she's not here, then it's your job to arrange which room they'll have!'

'Perhaps Greta will prefer her old room. I'll ask her.' She had blushed at his abruptness, and as she caught Luke's eyes she saw that he was almost scowling. It seemed that although he himself was not pleased with her he resented her father's manner which was causing Christine this discomfort.

'Aren't you going in to see them?' he enquired of Arthur. And when there was a glowering hesitation Luke added with a hint of censure, 'It's expected of you, Arthur, if only for courtesy's sake. Surely you're glad to see them?'

For answer he gave a deep sigh, glanced at Christine, hesitated a moment and then, 'Run along; tell them I'll be there in a few minutes.'

'Very well.' Her brow puckered in bewilderment at

his behaviour; she went slowly from the room, merely pulling the door to behind her without actually closing it. She was recalling Arthur's strangeness at the breakfast table on that particular morning last week when he had received the letter from Greta. Halfway through his breakfast he had seemed to become brooding, as if he had something lying heavily on his mind. And now . . . he was not in the least eager to come out of his study and welcome his daughter. There should have been hugs and kisses and many questions for Greta and Steve to answer. Instead, it would appear that Arthur had no enthusiasm for the meeting with the daughter he had not seen for just over six months.

Christine had just reached the door of the sitting room and was about to open it when she heard voices upraised—the shrill, high note so familiar when Greta was in a temper, and the angry voice of her husband. Quarrelling? Unwilling to go in, Christine turned away, and so absorbed was her mind on the two in there that she found herself back at the door of Arthur's study, which was slightly ajar as she had left it only a few seconds ago.

'They're not happy, you say!' It was Luke's disbelieving voice that drifted out to her as she was about to pass on with the intention of going out to the garden for a few minutes. But she stopped, held to the spot by some compelling force even though one half of her mind was urging her to move on. 'How the devil do you know that?'

'It came through in her letter—oh, nothing actually said but I could easily read between the lines. I can't think what in heaven's name has gone wrong, and I've enough on my mind with Loreen. Added to all this I'm not feeling myself at all these days, Luke.'

'It's a damnable situation! If Loreen were my wife I'd give her a damned good hiding!'

'And what would that solve? No, Luke, that's not the way to rectify anything. And to hell with Loreen and her damned lover! I've my daughter's troubles to cope with!'

'You could be mistaken.'

'Perhaps, but I don't hold out much hope.'

Trembling from head to foot, Christine managed at last to move on, down the corridor to the arched alcove off which were the bedrooms, Entering her own, she sank down on the bed, her mind in a chaotic muddle as she endeavoured to sort out what she had heard. Yet it was simple, and her mind became clear in seconds. Loreen definitely did have a lover, and Luke had obviously known it for some time, and secondly Greta and Steve had run into difficulties with their marriage— or so Arthur believed.

Chapter Six

Christine turned her head to stare at her companion. Her throat felt dry and in her violet eyes were dark shadows of near despair. 'You mean—you and Greta can't go on? You really mean it, Steve?'

He sighed and for a moment did not speak. He and Christine were strolling along the beach, their bodies warmed by the sun but in their hearts a coldness neither of them could dispel.

'I was madly in love with her,' he mused, a pained expression on his rugged face. 'Looking back now, I realise it was the sort of affair that had no foundation and it was bound to collapse.' He turned his head. 'No, Christine, we can't go on. Greta's impossible to live with and you must have known what I was letting myself in for.'

She made no answer to that; she owed a certain loyalty to her adoptive sister if only because it was her parents who had given her, Christine, a home. She said in a low despairing voice, 'What will you do, then, Steve?'

'It's up to Greta. She wants her freedom—says she ought never to have given it up yet awhile—until she had had her fling.'

'She actually said that?'

'As good as,' shrugged Steve. He stopped and turned to her. 'I know now that you had begged her to let you be a bridesmaid—'

'That's not important any more,' broke in Christine hastily. It was surprising how soon she had forgotten that desperate hurt. The tender years . . . Yes, that disappointment had taken on enormous proportions but only because she was—as Luke maintained—going through her tender years. But about Steve and her feelings for him Luke was wrong, mistaken in thinking this was calf love. It was real, alive, vital within her, and although she felt sorry about the broken marriage she was woman enough to see the future . . . and the silver beginning to show through the cloud that had descended upon her since the moment she had fallen in love with him. But the cloud was still very dark; Steve was still married and it would probably be two years before he was free. . . . The weight dropped on Christine's spirits again and she bit her lip, wondering why fate was so cruel, letting Steve marry Greta when she, Christine, could have made him deliriously happy.

And as though reading her thoughts, he said softly, a hand coming out to touch her cheek, 'I guess it was you, Christine, but I was fool enough to consider you far too young. In any case, Greta dazzled me and I believed myself the luckiest guy alive when she said she'd marry me.'

Christine's throat went dry again. 'You mean—you're saying . . . ?'

'I care for you, Christine. Oh, so much I thought of you after the wedding. You must have been in tears when Greta refused to let you be a bridesmaid—you should by rights have been the chief one. Yes,' he continued musingly, his eyes locked to Christine's and within their depths the sort of glazed look that told her his mind was not focussed on the present moment. 'So many times I thought of you, and I knew that you'd never have done a trick like that to Greta, had the positions been reversed. You're gentle, dear, and compassionate and understanding.'

He was with her now and profoundly aware of her beauty—the big violet eyes wide and sad, the tremulous quivering of the mouth and the delicate colour of her cheeks—pale and yet glowing with health as was her hair, gleaming in the sunlight and with that adorable half fringe that never would behave as she wanted it to. Steve touched it tenderly, and his fingers traced a line to her temple as if he was actually feeling the blue veins showing there, through the transparency of her skin. A quiver passed through her and when he bent to kiss her she wanted to let him, to feel his lips on hers in a *real* kiss, not those brotherly kisses she was used to receiving before his marriage and subsequent departure from the island. But Luke's face intruded, stern and forbidding, a glint in those tawny eyes . . . and disapproval written all over his face. The scar seemed to her imagination to be standing out, just as if Luke were being affected by some strong emotion. She shook her head to dispel the unwanted vision and stepped backwards at the same time.

'You mustn't kiss me,' she said.

'Why not? We care, Christine, so why pretend? I can see it in your eyes, have done for the past three days— No, darling, don't deny it! I have seen love for me in your eyes since the moment you heard Greta say, so harshly, that it was all over between her and me.'

Christine frowned at the memory. It was barely two hours after their arrival and they were having lunch. Luke had been persuaded to stay but he had contributed nothing to the conversation, which was strained to say the least. Greta was silent, Steve trying to converse with his father-in-law and Christine just sitting there feeling the food was choking her. Then suddenly, without even leading up to it, Greta had said to her father, 'You might as well know now as later. Steve and I are having marriage trouble.'

Arthur had said nothing, because of course he had guessed from Greta's letter that something was wrong with the marriage. Christine's eyes had met those of Luke; she read contempt, which she knew was for Greta and Steve, for marrying without making sure it would work—or, at least, have some chance of working. Then Christine saw a challenge in Luke's eyes, in that steely glint that was so often pronounced these days, and this time she knew it was for her—directed against her, more like, and she averted her face, quite unable to meet that challenge. Afterwards Luke had managed to get her alone for a few moments.

'Watch yourself,' he had advised. 'Don't go headlong into something you're likely to regret.' His voice had been hard, his eyes tempered steel and his jaw taut, inflexible . . . and almost frighteningly forbidding.

'I don't know what you mean,' she had begun.

But Luke had cut her short with an imperious flick of his hand and said, 'You know very well what I mean! Keep your head!' and with that he had swung away on his heel, said a brief and curt good-bye to Arthur and left. Christine had not seen him since; she did not even know if he was on the island or if he had gone off to Grand Bahama or Nassau . . . or perhaps Miami. . . .

'Christine . . . you're miles away.' Steve's voice recalled her and she forced a smile to her lips.

'I was thinking of how Greta told us all that the marriage had broken up. I suppose there was no sense in trying to be subtle about it,' she added. 'Luke was disgusted—'

'I saw that at once. But then, he's the kind who'd make absolutely sure. There'll be no wild and heady road to romance for him, no starry visions which could disintegrate like a vaporous film of starlit cloud.'

'You're saying he isn't romantic?' Christine wondered why the implication was resented.

'I expect he'll find romance, of a kind, one day, but—' Steve shook his head vigorously. 'He's the staid kind, Christine.' He looked at her curiously. 'You must have discovered this already, seeing that you and he are so close.'

Close . . .

'We've been drifting apart lately,' she reflected and a small sigh issued from her lips. 'He has a girl friend— but perhaps you know?'

'Greta said something about a girl in Miami—Clarice something or other.'

'I've met her.'

'What's she like?' Steve seemed slightly impatient, as if he wanted to talk of other things instead of wasting time on discussing a woman he had never met.

'Very beautiful,' was Christine's brief reply before,

abruptly, she changed the subject, suggesting they went along to the cafe and had morning coffee.

He readily agreed, and while they were drinking it he told Christine of his early disillusionment. 'Greta seemed cool even after the first week,' he said with a reflective frown. 'And a week later she was acting as if she were bored.'

'Bored, on her honeymoon?' gasped Christine, picturing herself in Greta's place and knowing it would be sheer heaven to have Steve sharing a honeymoon with her.

'I realise now that I knew absolutely nothing about her,' he said.

And it suddenly occurred to Christine that he knew even less about her. And what did she know about him? But that was of no matter and she shrugged it off as of no importance whatsoever. She loved him, fiercely, and with a love that would last forever. Oh, yes, she knew her own mind, and if she and Steve married they would stay married; there would be no repetition of what had happened now, between him and Greta.

Greta stood on the patio clad in briefs and a top that was merely two triangles covering her breasts. Her skin was a glorious deep amber, gleaming in the sun, her shoulders sloped in a way which, thought Christine, must be a sort of erotic temptation to any man.

Greta turned on realising she was no longer alone. 'You,' she remarked briefly.

'David and Martha are having a party and they told me to tell you you're invited.'

'I hope you didn't accept for me,' snapped Greta

with the accustomed frown which Christine knew so well.

'I did, as a matter of fact. You used to like their parties.'

'I'm not in a party mood,' returned Greta in loose and edgy tones. 'You'd no right to accept on my behalf and so you can just get out of it the best way you can.' She swung around and again Christine was staring at her back. Greta was looking out over the white-sanded beach to the sea, aquamarine and glittering in the afternoon sunlight. A yacht rode the waves gracefully, its white sails fluttering in the breeze. The horizon was dark beneath a cloudless sky of azure blue and all was so quiet and peaceful that it seemed impossible that friction and dislike could exist—and yet they did. Greta had not even tried to hide her dislike of Christine and yesterday, after watching her and Steve laughing together, she asked Christine if she didn't mind taking on another girl's castoff. Christine had flinched and it had been very difficult not to retaliate in some hateful way which, she knew, she would regret afterwards, if only because she had lowered her pride. She managed to refrain but the look she had cast at Greta had left that girl in no doubt as to what Christine thought about her.

The atmosphere was always electric, more especially when Arthur was there because he had angrily told the couple to stop being stupid and to give the marriage a fair trial. Greta resented any mention of what she should or should not do, while Steve, usually possessed of a fair share of self-confidence, seemed to shrink into himself when in the old man's company. Christine wondered when they would leave. It would seem that they must go back to their home, if only to sort everything out, but Steve had hinted that he might go and stay with his parents. They were away on holiday at present and so Steve was granted a respite, but he was gravely perturbed because his mother had always adored Greta. As for Greta's immediate plans—she had been noncommittal when her father had asked her what they were.

'What shall you do tonight, then?' Christine wanted to know.

'I suppose Steve's going to the party?'

'He might,' quietly and with a touch of hesitation.

'Have a nice time,' returned Greta sarcastically. She swung around again and there was a sneering edge to her voice when she spoke. 'Don't you both wish Steve were free?'

'Don't say such things! You ought to take your father's advice and try to make something of the marriage.'

'Who are you trying to deceive?' The sneer was on Greta's lips now. 'You must have talked about us— Steve and me. And you both wish he were free.'

'I asked what you were going to do tonight?'

'It has nothing to do with you.'

'It's lonely here on your own,' began Christine. She wondered why she should trouble herself about any loneliness which Greta might feel. 'Father's going to be out—'

'I know; he told me.'

'Well, then?'

'I shan't be lonely, and in any case, it has nothing to do with you. I've just told you so.' Again Greta turned her back. Christine's mouth set and she left the patio without another word.

Steve was in the sitting room as she entered. He had been over to visit a friend and Christine was surprised to see him back so soon.

'It was becoming too much of a strain,' he offered before Christine could voice the question that came instantly to her mind. 'Trying to be cheerful, to appear the happy husband. Richard's not a fool, and added to that, he never did like Greta; so I'd like to bet he's already guessed something's wrong.'

'You'll have to tell people,' began Christine tentatively, her thoughts speeding to his mother, who would be heartbroken at this turn of events. 'It's bound to leak out soon.'

He glanced at her. 'You're thinking of Mother?'

'And others, Steve. This is a small island, remember.'

'Perhaps Arthur's already given a few hints.' His voice was low, his mouth sagging at the corners. 'If only I could put the clock back!'

She looked away, unable to bear the sight of his distress. That he was no longer in love with Greta was plain, but that he was deeply touched and upset was equally plain. His whole life had been turned upside down and Christine supposed his anxiety could also stem from the fact that his prestige would suffer, for everyone must regard him as stupid to have gone into marriage and, within six months, be having a divorce.

'Christine,' he groaned. 'Oh, my dear . . .' She wanted to go to him, to fling her arms around him, offering the comfort which he craved. But something seemed to be preventing her from following this very natural impulse . . . something that baffled her because Luke stood like an invincible barrier just as if he were controlling her by sheer physical compulsion.

'Don't go headlong into something you're likely to regret. . . .' His words rang in her head. She could see his forbidding countenance and those tawny eyes . . . accusing eyes. . . .

'Are you going to the party tonight?' She spoke merely to break the silence and frowned when Steve shook his head.

'I don't think so, Christine.' He managed a thin smile. 'How about you and me going off somewhere to dine?'

'Wherever we go it'll be common knowledge by this time tomorrow,' she pointed out sensibly. 'We're known in all the restaurants.'

'We could go to my home. There'll be the servants, but they'll not gossip.'

His home . . . A few hours alone with him. Every quivering nerve in her body yearned for an interlude like that. Yet she heard herself say, 'It wouldn't be right, Steve, and in any case I've promised Martha that I'll be at her party.'

'You could phone her, as I shall.'

Again temptation loomed . . . and again there was Luke. . . . Sudden anger stormed into her mind. Luke! He had no right to be troubling her like this—just because he had thought fit to proffer that stern warning! She would *not* be influenced by him or anything he had said, or would say in the future!

'Yes,' she agreed, rather in the manner of one burning her boats irrevocably, 'I'll dine with you at your house.'

'I'll go and arrange everything,' he said, 'and come back for you later.'

She was in an evening gown of pale mauve taffeta trimmed with tiny pearl beads at the neck and waist. She regarded herself in the mirror and liked what she saw. The dress made her look older, more sophisticated. She was eager for Steve to come and fetch her.

'You're going to a barbecue party in that?'

It was the disbelieving voice of Greta that caused Christine to wheel about, her heart giving an uncomfortable little jerk. She coloured, saw her sister's eyes narrow and said swiftly, 'Why not? I like long dresses.'

'Not for a barbecue, you don't. In any case, that's far too formal. Just where are you going, Christine?'

'To—to Martha's party.'

'You're a total failure as a liar,' sneered Greta coming into the bedroom and standing just inside the door. 'You're going out with *my* husband, aren't you?'

'I—I—'

'You rotten little snake in the grass! I always suspected that you had a crush on him and would have stolen him from me if you could! Well, miss, you're not going!'

Christine had been almost cowering under the onslaught but now she straightened up to her full height and her eyes flashed fire. 'And who's to stop me going?' she demanded wrathfully.

'I shall stop you.' Greta's voice was dangerously soft, her advance slow and threatening. Christine stood her ground, her shoulders erect, her eyes sparkling with challenge. 'I'll tear that dress off your back!'

'Try it!' But in spite of her confident words Christine

felt the colour drain from her face. She was alone in the house with Greta, but for the servants, and she knew she would never call out if Greta should carry out her threat, or attempt to do so.

'You are not going out with my husband!'

'This is a dog-in-the-manger attitude,' flashed Christine. 'You don't want to go out with him yourself and yet you can't bear to think he's going out with someone else!'

Greta stopped very close to Christine, her eyes glittering in the most frightening way. That she was being held firmly in the grip of a violent emotion was plain, and with a flashback of memory Christine was seeing her as she had behaved a few years ago when she had been in an argument with her father. She had become hysterical and then aggressive, actually making an attack on him, and Christine had watched, terrified, as Arthur had gripped Greta's hands and held them to her sides. There had been a fearful struggle, with Greta seeming to have acquired abnormal strength. At last her father had slapped her and she had fled, screaming, to her room.

And now she appeared to be on the verge of a similar outbreak and Christine, no longer brave and defiant, was darting glances at the door, assessing her chance of getting through it to the safety of the corridor and the hall.

Greta moved again and Christine swung an arm to ward her off, using all her strength. The action took Greta by surprise, and in the fleeting moment when she was off balance and trying to regain it Christine had raced past her and was out of the room. But as she reached the hall she tripped over the hem of her dress and crashed, headlong, to the floor. It was at that moment, with Greta almost upon her, and screaming out imprecations, that the front door opened and Luke stood there, his tawny eyes widening in bewilderment. But his reaction was swift in that he was stooping to pick Christine up within seconds of his entering the house.

'What the devil's going on?' he demanded of Greta.

'She—that *thing*—' Greta pointed, her face blue with fury at being prevented from carrying out her intended assault. 'That—viper! She's made a date with *my* husband! I'd have marked her face if you hadn't come in! And what are you doing here anyway?' she shouted. 'Walking in as if you own the place!'

'The door was ajar. I'd been ringing and had no answer—' He stopped, frowning heavily. He glanced down at the girl he had rescued, taking in the evening dress and dainty shoes. 'You were going out with Steve?' He seemed to be affording her a sort of cool attention, his accents smooth so that nothing could be gathered as regards his inner thoughts about this situation.

'I *am* going out with Steve,' answered Christine unsteadily. She shuddered against Luke's hard body, every nerve rioting.

'They're having an affair!' shouted Greta, her hands clenching and unclenching in fury. 'She wanted him right from the first!'

'Luke . . . please take me to Steve's house.' Christine knew full well how Luke would feel but she cherished the vague hope that he would do as she asked.

'Why are you here?' demanded Greta in quivering

tones. 'I've asked you once! Why don't you answer me!'

'I came to take Christine to the party.'

'Martha's and David's?' Christine looked up into a face of unsmiling disapproval. 'You're invited too?' She had thought he was still away.

'Why the surprise?' returned Luke coldly. 'They're my friends, so you ought to have known I'd be invited.' Again he glanced at her attire. 'You'd better go and change into something more suitable to a barbecue,' he said and released her. His eyes were on Greta as he added softly, 'Either you stay here with me while I wait for Christine, or I accompany her to her room. Take your choice.'

So cool, and yet the firmness was apparent, and after a small hesitation, Greta flung at him, 'Go up with her! I'm not staying here, in your company, a moment longer!'

Christine turned to Luke as he entered her bedroom close on her heels. 'I've made a date with Steve. We're dining at his house.'

'You're going to the barbecue with me.' Walking over to a chair, Luke sat down, hitching up a trouser leg and leaning back comfortably against the dainty satin upholstery.

'But I've made the date!'

'Which you ought not to have done. It's a date you're not going to keep, Christine, so forget it!'

Anger brought tears flooding into her eyes. 'You can't dictate to me!' she cried. 'I'm my own mistress and I'm nearly nineteen! I won't be dictated to by you or anyone else!' She paused, but what she was hoping for she did not know. She ought to be conversant enough with Luke's firmness by now. Yes, the compression of the mouth and the narrowing of those tawny eyes. The flexing of the jaw and rigidity of the face as a whole. 'Luke,' she pleaded, 'take me to Steve. We want to be together—'

'If you don't get a move on,' broke in Luke, glancing at his watch, 'it's going to be half over before we get there.'

'I—' She pouted, then stamped her foot. 'I've phoned Martha to say I can't come!'

'That doesn't matter. She'll be delighted that you made it after all.'

'Steve—'

'I'll phone him on our way out.' He glanced around and saw the phone. 'I'll do it now,' he amended and rose from the chair.

'You can't!' she cried in protest. 'I won't let you!'

He stopped and turned to her, his face set in wrathful lines. 'Christine, I've had enough! Now, do you get that dress off or do I take it off for you?' He was towering over her in what she could only describe as a threatening and domineering manner and the tears began to flow, running unhindered on to her dress. 'Well, answer me!'

She sagged and wept into her hands. 'I'll change,' she faltered and went with dragging feet to the wardrobe. After choosing a pair of bright blue cotton pants and a short-sleeved blouse, she went into the bathroom, not bothering to close the door properly. She listened to Luke on the telephone, hearing the harsh words spoken in a slightly raised voice.

'No, she will not be coming! Christine's going to the

party with me. Steve—keep away from her! Do you understand? I am ordering, not telling! Keep away from Christine!' A silence followed and then, 'Isn't it my business? And what makes you think that? It is very much my business! I shall protect her—' Another silence after Steve had obviously interrupted. Then Christine heard, 'From you, but from herself as well!' The receiver was replaced and, peeping out, Christine saw Luke go over to the window and stare out through the mosquito netting. He was furious. . . . What had she done to their relationship this time? A flood of remorse mingled with a great wave of sadness and the tears came faster than before. Luke's face was pale and rigid when at last she came from the bathroom knuckling her eyes.

'All these tears for a man you can't have!' His hard eyes drilled into her. 'Have you considered what people would say if you had your way over this?'

She was silent, wanting desperately to tell him that the tears this time were not for Steve at all but shed because of her own widening of the rift that had come between Luke and herself. She glanced into those hard eyes and tried to tell him, but his anger was causing a terrible choking sensation in her throat so that words were impossible to articulate.

'I'm—r-ready,' she managed at last, and after he had moved impatiently to let her know he was waiting.

In the car she again knew the desperate urge to tell him how she felt, and to tell him she was sorry, but on glancing sideways at his stern forbidding profile, her courage failed her and she remained silent. The atmosphere thickened and the pain in her heart was excruciating. She felt she would want to die if Luke cast her off altogether, if he should lose all interest in her and begin to treat her as he treated so many other women—with disinterest and often contempt should they try to attract his attention. Since ever she had known him he had seemed not to have any interest in women, not until Clarice and that, she felt, was a superficial attachment from which he could cut adrift without the merest hint of a qualm.

No interest in women . . . But yet he had always had an interest in her, she mused. Yes, indeed, always he had been keenly interested in all she did or said. He had not once rejected her or held aloof from her at those times when she sought his tenderness or compassion. And she had now begun to realise just how patient he had always been with her, how ready to listen, to comfort, to give her affection and love. Love . . . He loved her she was sure, as a big brother, of course, or a father. It was a beautiful love, selfless and sincere. Christine felt the sting of tears behind her eyes, and when eventually the car was crunching to a stop beneath some flamboyant trees outside the ranch-style villa owned by David and Martha Smilley she turned impulsively and said in quivering tones that yet held the softness of a plea, 'Luke—I'm sorry for—for—for losing my temper. There wasn't any excuse . . . oh, Luke, don't be angry with me! I couldn't bear it.'

He stopped the car and switched off the engine. She felt his strong arm come around her shoulders and instinctively and with a heart bursting with gratitude she leant against him, drawing on his strength for comfort.

'Forget it, my Chris,' he said gently and his cool lips

caressed her cheek. 'You're such a baby, dear. Grow up, my little girl—grow up quickly so that you can see things straight.'

'See things straight?' she echoed, baffled. 'Luke, you're talking in riddles again.'

He sighed. Trouble was, he thought, she had grown used to regarding him as a guardian or uncle, a man to lean upon and that was all.

'One day, my Chris, you'll not say that, because you will have left the tender years behind you,'

'But after one's teens one begins to get old.' She snuggled close, savouring the delightful smell of after-shave mingling with the nice, clean odour of newly laundered linen.

'Not old, dear, just a little bit more mature.' His voice took on a tender note as he added, 'You'll never grow old, Chris. At ninety you'll still be young.'

She sighed against him and her arm crept up and around his neck. 'I love you, Luke. You know that, don't you?' Strangely, Steve was as vague as the misted heavens at this moment. She was glad she was with Luke and going to the party.

'Do you love me, dear? Are you quite sure?' The words came from the very depths of his heart but she did not understand what it was that he really wanted in her answer.

'Of course!' she returned eagerly. 'You're my haven, my sanctuary from pain and from the hurts that others sometimes give me. I shall always come to you, Luke, when I need sympathy.' Lifting her face, she kissed him lightly on the lips. 'Oh, Luke, you were so right in making me come here with you!'

'You think that?' He seemed rather taken aback for a moment. 'What about your date with Steve?' He spoke slowly, as if the mention of Steve came unwillingly.

'I feel sorry for him, Luke; he's very sad.' She ought to add that Steve loved her but, somehow, she actually flinched at the idea of saying anything that would annoy Luke. 'He'll be on his own this evening.'

'He can go out; there's always plenty to do on Pirates' Cay.'

Which was quite true. And as Steve was so well known on the island he'd soon find someone to talk to if he decided to go out to dinner at one of the restaurants.

'Well, dear, we had better be going in.' But Luke drew her close to him and, taking her chin in his hand in the most proprietorial way, he kissed her hard on the mouth. For a long moment she stayed close even after he had slackened his hold. A hand went tentatively to her lips and a finger caressed them wonderingly. Even yet again she was aware of changes in Luke . . . and in herself. . . .

Chapter Seven

The barbecue was a lighthearted affair and was held in the grounds of the lovely villa on the seafront. The night was warm and balmy, with a full moon sailing in a purple sky thick with stars. As they walked about among the hibiscus bushes socialising, Christine did wonder why she wasn't thinking about Steve and worrying over his disappointment at not seeing her tonight. She supposed the scene with Greta had affected her so badly that all she had wanted was the comfort which Luke could give her. That seemed to be the only explanation she could find to account for the way she was feeling. She was happy here with Luke, and she knew she was the envy of several young women present tonight.

There was Jenny Cavendish who had made no secret of her liking for Luke; she was a charming girl, but although Luke was always gracious towards her he had never shown any real interest. Another girl who would very much have liked to gain Luke's interest was Paula Reeves, daughter of a millionaire hotel owner and as beautiful as they come. Christine recalled one particular occasion when Luke had danced with Paula; she had flirted with him, had used every trick she could command and Christine, feeling piqued for no reason she could explain, had said pettishly to Luke, 'That girl's a flirt! I don't know how you could be so nice with her!' And Luke had glanced at Christine very strangely indeed but made no comment on the complaint she had made.

'Are you enjoying it, Chris?' Luke's quiet voice severed her musings and she glanced up with a ready smile.

'Of course. These cutlets are delicious!'

'I agree.' His reply was brief and Christine had the impression that he had almost said, 'Very different fare from what you'd have had at Steve's.' But he had refrained because he never spoke of Steve these days and she felt sure he was hoping she would forget him. And perhaps she would have, she thought, if the marriage had turned out right. But now . . . There was a chance that she and Steve would get together and make a wonderful go of *their* marriage. 'What are you thinking?' Luke's voice again. He might almost be able to read her mind, the way he had broken into her reflections.

'It wasn't important,' she replied, glad of the darkness which hid from his perceptive eyes the fact that she had lied. Steve was the most important person in her life.

She and Luke had wandered from the brilliantly lighted area to a warm, starlit clearing beyond the formal parts of the gardens. Here was the natural vegetation of the island, mainly palms and tall pines, and here and there a coloured electric bulb had been fixed to a branch so that the red and green and blue lights intermingled to give a soft romantic glow to supplement the light from the moon and a million stars flickering around it.

They found a seat and took possession of it, sitting with their plates on their knees, eating in a companionable silence, the kind of silence which they both enjoyed. For Christine it was the closeness of her companion, the knowledge that he was there for her to confide in if she wished. Tonight, she felt an added depth to this almost unreal hush that lay between them, as if magical vibrations were passing from one mind and body to the other.

'I feel strange,' she whispered, not meaning to voice what was in her mind.

'Strange? In what way?'

'It's—it's magical out here tonight.'

'No different from any other night of its kind. You're on an exotic island, remember.'

'I know—but—' She raised her face in the cool moonlight. 'Don't you feel anything, Luke?'

'Such as?'

'A closeness between you and me— A different closeness, I mean,' she added hurriedly.

'Different . . .' The dear familiar voice held an odd inflection. 'Many things are different between you and me, Chris. Time alone creates changes.'

Something in his voice that was significant, but she failed to catch it. She said with a sudden frown, 'You enjoy talking in riddles, don't you, Luke?'

His slow smile did something to her it had never done before. 'I merely stated a fact: that time alone creates changes. We have to accept them and live with them— or we can reject them and veer onto a different course. Either way the changes play a significant part in our lives, and sometimes the veering of a different course can bring us nothing but heartache and regret.'

So he wasn't talking in riddles now.

'You're referring to the way Steve and I are with one another?'

'I warned you not to do anything you'd regret.' Luke's voice was terse now and Christine found herself changing the subject.

'When are you going to Grand Bahama again? I loved it there. Have you decided to buy a house— You mentioned something about it, didn't you?'

For a moment he made no reply but just looked at her, and it was plain that he was well aware of the reason for this apparent interest in the house he intended buying on Grand Bahama Island. 'I shall be going next week. Perhaps, seeing that you like it so much, you'd come with me? I intend staying for about ten days.'

She shook her head immediately. 'Not this time, Luke,' was all she said and the silence fell like a cloak around them again, but this time its effect was smothering.

'Shall we go back to the others?' His voice was still terse as he rose from the seat. 'We haven't spoken to Martha yet.'

'I didn't see either her or David when we first arrived, and when I eventually did see them they were far too busy.'

'Slaving over that hot charcoal grill. They've always insisted on doing the cooking themselves, as you know.'

Conventional talk . . . Where had the closeness gone? Christine sighed with regret and knew that she alone was to blame for this chilly atmosphere that had replaced the intimate warmth of a few minutes ago.

Martha came up to them immediately they reached the swimming pool. 'We were so glad you could make it after all, Christine,' she said, her round homely face wreathed in smiles of pleasure. 'What was it? You merely rang and told David you weren't able to come, after all.'

At a loss for words Christine sent Luke an imploring glance. And as always he came to her rescue. 'Christine felt she ought not to come without Greta, but I persuaded her.'

Coerced, you mean, said Christine with her eyes.

'Greta . . . and Steve? They wanted to be alone, I suppose?'

'Something of the kind,' agreed Luke in an expressionless voice.

'I accepted for her and I ought not to have done,' put in Christine apologetically.

'Well, never mind, so long as you two are here.' Martha, approaching forty but looking rather older because of her chubby face and rounded figure, was a Bahamian and so was David. They ran a general store on Pirates' Cay and were about to buy another one on Grand Bahama Island. She and her husband were famous for their parties, their going to a great deal of trouble and always making sure the food was delicious and plentiful, with gallons of champagne flowing in addition to other wines and beer and liqueurs. 'Have a lovely time, won't you? I must be off or David'll be telling me I'm shirking!'

'She's super!' exclaimed Christine. 'I don't know how Greta could resist coming.'

'Have you any idea when her mother's coming back from her . . . holiday?'

The hesitation . . . Where was Loreen? In New York with her boyfriend? Last time she went away it was because she wasn't feeling well and the doctor had recommended a cruise.

'No, I haven't any idea. Father's becoming impatient, but he's scarcely ever in at nights now, so he's certainly not feeling lonely.' Her voice was edged with sadness and Luke slipped an arm about her shoulders.

'Stop worrying,' he advised, 'because you can't alter anything.'

'So much is going wrong,' she mused, falling into step as he urged her towards the place where the grill was glowing and appetising smells pervading the area all around it. David was browning sausages and he smiled and handed them some as they held out their plates.

'The sauces are over there, on that table.'

'Thanks, David, but these don't need sauces.' Luke chatted for a few minutes and Christine's thoughts sped to the shop they intended to buy, and she wondered if they would eventually move to Grand Bahama Island. She would miss them. . . . Changes again! If only she could halt them; if only things would stay as they were. But no. She wanted certain changes, for she wanted to become Steve's wife. She was madly in love with him . . . yet she was enjoying herself with Luke. . . .

'Come on, dear, we ought to be socialising.' Luke slid an arm about her shoulders again. She became vitally conscious of the warmth of his hand, the gentle —and probably unconscious—caress of his fingers on her nape.

It was much later that they again found themselves

straying away from the other guests, from the lights and chatter and the dying charcoal fires.

'I feel heady,' she admitted. 'Champagne's *beautiful*!'

'You didn't overdo it, though.'

'Only because you wouldn't let me.'

'I'm gratified to know you obey me,' was his dry response to that.

'Not always willingly,' she returned with an arch smile and lift of her shoulders. 'You domineer over me, Luke!'

'You don't resent it, though.' They were well away now, strolling into the darkness beneath the tamarind trees backing the shoreline. The light of the moon was a spread of silver over the sea whose surface was a gentle ripple of silk. Luke sought her hand as the ground became a little stony. She curled her fingers around it and happiness flowed through her.

'I expected you to deny my assertion,' she murmured, sending him a swift oblique glance and noticing with a little sense of shock that the tiny wrinkles etching the corners of his eyes were becoming more pronounced. But it was the sun, she decided, not a sign of age. Twenty-seven . . . Nine years older than she. It had once seemed a lot but now . . .

Steve was seventeen years older than she—almost twice her age.

'Assertion?' belatedly from Luke, whose voice had a faraway tone to it. 'What assertion?'

'You weren't listening. It doesn't matter.'

'If I domineer over you,' he said, 'it's for your own good.'

'Oh, so you *were* listening!' She laughed. 'For my

own good . . .' she murmured. 'Will you always domineer over me?' she asked and her brows drew together because she had to admit that, once she was married to Steve, Luke would be forced to drop his mastery over her.

'I don't really domineer,' he denied in gentle tones. 'Someone, dear, has to take an interest in you, now haven't they?' He stopped and placed his hands on her shoulders. 'You don't receive much attention at home these days,' he added and it was now his turn to frown.

Christine was nodding her head reflectively. 'That's why I need you so much.' She sighed. 'You've become my only prop, Luke.' She lifted her eyes to his, eyes limpid in the moonlight escaping through the feathery foliage of the tamarind trees. Luke's frown smoothed out and his slow smile came. He was fascinated by the seductiveness of her lips, parted softly as if to accept a kiss. He sighed and thought of Steve. Then the man's image was dismissed and Luke was bending his dark head. Quivers of expectation sped along her spine as she felt the caress of his cool clean breath on her cheek. His lips found hers, gentle at first, but as before his ardour was spurred by the behaviour of Christine herself as, in her bewildered and floundering way, she was reciprocating, physically and emotionally aroused, and as he slid his hands with gentle, possessive slowness right down her back she felt faintly shocked at the knowledge that she hoped the nearness of her body excited him.

'Come on,' he suddenly said in a brusque voice. 'This is no way to contribute to the success of a party.'

He drew away; she knew a sense of loss . . . of a

moment in time which had escaped her grasp, a moment that could have meant so much. . . .

He was later troubled about leaving her at the door of Cassia Lodge. 'Will Greta be in bed?' he murmured almost to himself, his eyes sliding to the window of the room which used to be hers.

'I'll be all right.' Christine spoke lightly to hide the unease which his softly spoken words had engendered. There was a pensive silence before he spoke again.

'I'll come in with you, Chris. And if Arthur's not home yet I'll wait until he is.'

Always concerned for her . . . Christine swallowed hard and slipped a hand into his as they stood close together by the door.

'I'll be all right,' she said again even while hoping he would ignore her self-assured words and come in with her. For some indefinable reason she wanted to keep him with her, a reason which, she felt sure, had nothing at all to do with any fear she might have regarding her sister.

'You might not be all right,' he began. 'Have you a key?'

Christine produced it and he unlocked the door. There was no sign of life until the appearance of a maid.

'Is Mr. Mead in?' enquired Luke and the girl shook her head.

'He's late, Mr. Curtis. I had expected him to be in for dinner.' She sounded a trifle worried and this passed itself on to Christine.

'It's almost midnight, Luke. Do you think something might have happened to him?'

'He's probably had dinner with friends and stayed on chatting.' He added after a slight pause, 'Mr. and Mrs. Walworth—they're in?'

The girl's face took on a wooden expression. 'Mr. Walworth came and packed some of his things.'

'Yes?' prompted Luke.

'He took a suitcase—er—I got the impression that he was going to stay at his parents' house.' She was embarrassed but for all that, Luke surmised that she had not kept the circumstance to herself. All Arthur's staff would know that Steve had left his wife.

'And Mrs. Walworth?'

Again the girl paused. 'She went out and later phoned to say she was staying the night with a friend.'

'What a business!' Luke was saying a few minutes later when he and Christine were alone in the sitting room. His face was set, his eyes dark and unreadable. He had been standing by the window but he came towards where she was sitting on the couch. He stood above her, a towering giant looking suddenly angry.

'I ought to take you out of this!' he said harshly. 'Chris, will you come and live at my house?'

'Live . . . !' Staggered by the suggestion she could only stare, dumbfounded, for fully twenty seconds. 'Leave my parents? Luke, what are you saying?'

'This family's getting itself into the kind of coil I don't want you to be a part of.' Imperious his voice and compelling. Not for the first time Christine was impressed by his manner of authority, his almost arrogant domination. It was just as if he were in sole charge of her, body and soul! Her chin went up.

'Whatever troubles they are in, Luke, they *are* my family—the only family I have. I ought to be sharing their troubles, not running out on them. Why, you said yourself that Arthur needs me.' Funny, she mused with a frown, but recently she had come to regard her adoptive father as a man somewhat remote, so that she found herself more easily thinking of him as 'Arthur' rather then her father or her uncle.

'I admit saying he needs you, but things are happening that worry me. He's never in, and Loreen's scarcely ever at home. And now you have this trouble between Greta and Steve.' He strode away towards the drinks cabinet. 'I shall speak to Arthur,' he decided as he sought for a glass. 'Something has to be done about you.'

'I *am* almost nineteen,' she reminded him.

'And more like sixteen!' Anger edged his tone and she had the impression that he wished she were older than her age rather than younger. She resented his words, though, because she was sure she did not act like a sixteen-year-old. However, she had no chance of voicing a protest because at that moment the front door was heard to bang and Arthur came into the room.

'Hello.' He seemed only vaguely surprised to see Luke there, pouring himself a drink. 'Where is everybody?'

'If you mean Greta and Steve,' answered Luke crisply, 'neither is coming home tonight.'

Arthur looked blank. 'I don't understand.'

Was he troubled? wondered Christine as she looked at him closely. He had certainly been troubled about Greta and Steve at first. He seemed to be acquiring a hard shell of indifference, she thought, and sighed for the days that had gone.

'Steve's left Greta from what I can gather. And Greta's staying the night with a friend.'

'And my wife's away, too,' added Arthur broodingly. He held out his hand for the brandy which Luke had just poured and swallowed it all in one swift draught.

Christine stared, then turned her eyes to Luke. He said quietly, 'Do you want a drink, Christine?'

She shook her head miserably. 'No, thank you, Luke.' In all this, she thought, only Luke offered any form of stability. He was solid and firm, like a rock that no forces of nature can make any sort of impression upon. He was her pillar of strength in a world that was beginning to disintegrate around her.

Luke poured another brandy and sipped it slowly. Arthur had taken possession of a deep armchair; he looked almost desolate as he stared in front of him, appearing to be oblivious of any other presence in the room. Luke walked to the fireplace and stood with his back to the grate. His quiet, finely modulated voice cut into the oppressive silence as he commented, 'I don't particularly care for the changes that are occurring here.'

'No more do I.' Arthur had glanced up in surprise. 'Just what are you getting at, Luke?'

'I'll not beat about the bush, Arthur.' Luke's voice was clipped. 'I want to take Christine out of this.'

She flashed him a glance, her nerves feeling shredded. 'I don't want to go with you,' she began but Arthur was speaking too and she broke off.

'You mean—you want to marry her?'

'Marry!' she ejaculated, eyes widely staring. 'Father —what a thing to say!' She felt the blood surge into her cheeks.

'That,' Luke was saying slowly, 'might be a very good idea.'

'A—!' Her eyes flew open. So he would even go to the lengths of marrying her just to protect her! He would sacrifice his own happiness, his chance of a real marriage, just to save her from this situation which he knew was oppressing her. Her feelings were mixed; for while with one part of her she warmed to him for this willing sacrifice, with the other she was aware of a sense of pique at his authoritative way of assuming he could just come along and calmly take control of her life. 'It certainly is not a good idea!' Her eyes met his in a challenging look. He knew very well that she was in love with Steve, and that she was eager eventually to marry him. Luke flexed his mouth but made no comment.

'I must admit I'm becoming worried about her.' Arthur spoke to Luke just as if Christine hadn't been sitting there at all. 'As you say, changes are occurring here that are definitely not good, and I've been thinking lately that Christine ought not to be involved—'

'Why not?' she broke in vehemently. 'I'm part of the family and so your troubles are my troubles.'

'Family?' Arthur lifted his brows. 'We're no longer a family, Christine.'

She fell silent, her eyes filling up. For what he said was right. They were no longer a family—at least, not a united one.

'What's wrong, Arthur?' Luke asked, his tawny eyes concerned.

'Everything, Luke.' The older man's whole manner was bleak. 'I've just said we're not a family any more. There's nothing to keep us together—not a thread of love or respect to hold us. Loreen's obviously . . .' He tailed off, looking at Christine.

'I know, Father.' She spoke quietly, glancing away.

'Yes.' He sighed. 'You must have guessed. You're not obtuse.'

'Are you saying that Loreen wants a separation?' Luke's voice carried a harsh inflection.

'I was about to say that she's obviously intending to continue with this affair, so as I don't intend to be made a complete fool of, I'm considering suing for a divorce.'

Christine and Luke exchanged glances. She had never seen his eyes quite so hard, nor his mouth so ruthlessly tight. She shuddered, having no difficulty in picturing Loreen's fate had it been someone like Luke to whom she was married.

'So everything's gone,' stated Luke. 'As you say, the family no longer exists.'

'Greta and Steve are having a divorce. She's met someone else—'

'Met someone else!' gasped Christine disbelievingly. 'Already?'

Arthur ignored that, appearing to be impatient with the question. 'As for me—well, I'm thinking of retiring. I haven't been too well lately and if I want to live a bit longer I've to take things easy.'

'You've seen a doctor?' Christine spoke accusingly. 'Why didn't you tell me?'

'What difference could it have made?' He was still impatient. 'You couldn't have mended anything.'

'I'd rather know if you're ill,' she said. She glanced at Luke and knew she needed him more at this moment than ever before. Yet her thoughts were scattered, conflicting with one another. Luke was her prop, and yet for some reason she half regarded him as her enemy. In this throbbing despair caused by what Arthur had been saying she was filled with a sense of finality as far as her life with him and his wife was concerned. So that left Luke on whom she could lean . . . but Luke had no sympathy with her attitude towards Steve, no understanding of the fact that she was in love with him. She felt a hollowness in the pit of her stomach, knew she was pale of face and desolate of expression.

She could not help wondering what she would do if Luke were suddenly to disappear from her life. She knew of course that there was no such possibility. He had just suggested she marry him and, therefore, he could not have much feeling for the girl in Miami.

'I think,' he was saying, 'that under the circumstances Christine should stay with me, at least for a while.'

She thought of Steve and knew that if she went to stay with Luke she would have difficulty in seeing him.

'There's no reason why I should leave Cassia Lodge,' she said, but her heart was heavy. What was there for her at Cassia Lodge any more? That sense of finality enveloped her again. 'Father, what are you intending to do? I mean, when you retire?'

'I shall retire very soon,' he told her significantly, 'and live in England with my widowed sister.'

A silence fell upon the room. It was Luke who broke it. 'In that case, Arthur, you will agree that Christine must come to me.'

She was dumb now, steeped in misery.

'It would certainly be a good idea—'

'Have I no say?' she cried, valiantly fighting the tears

that threatened. 'After all, it's my life—my future you're arranging. Father, what makes you suppose I want to live with Luke?'

'There isn't anywhere else for you *to* live,' he answered flatly.

And suddenly she was admitting that he cared nothing for her now. Once he had cared but so much had happened to him recently that he had become like someone numbed of all feeling. It wasn't that he was acting in a heartless manner on purpose, she decided. But the time seemed to have come when all he wanted was to find peace of mind, and in his present state the only way was to put four thousand miles between him and Cassia Lodge and its memories.

'Come to me for the time being, dear,' she heard Luke say quietly. 'I know why you don't want to come but we can deal with that later.' He sipped his brandy and she watched his long brown fingers holding the glass. She herself was becoming numbed, devoid of any conscious emotions. She closed her eyes tightly because the tears were so very close to falling.

'Deal with what later?' Arthur was asking in a puzzled tone.

'It's nothing,' began Luke when Christine interrupted him.

'I love Steve,' she admitted flatly. 'And he loves me. Luke doesn't like the idea—'

'You and Steve!' Arthur stared in disbelief. 'My God, Christine, what are you saying?'

'It's calf love,' interposed Luke tightly. 'A crush, nothing more.'

'What is this all about?' demanded Arthur, glowering at Christine as though he hated her. 'Answer me!' he snapped, 'at once!'

'Why the devil did you have to mention it?' gritted Luke with a flash of censure in his eyes and Christine bit her lip.

'I'm sorry,' she muttered contritely. 'It was a mistake.'

'One that you've committed! And I want to know more about it!' Arthur continued to subject her to that glowering look. 'How long has this been going on?'

'It hasn't been going on—!' Christine felt the ragged abrasion of her nerve ends would result in her having a fit of hysterics—in which case Luke would be sure to take charge and cure her in the most effective way.

'It's infatuation,' intervened Luke, his glance contemptuous. 'Infatuation and perhaps habit,' he added cynically.

Christine's cheeks burned. 'It's no such thing!' she flashed. 'Neither of you knows how Steve and I feel!'

'Steve,' said Arthur between his teeth, 'happens to be your sister's husband!'

'Greta always maintained that I wasn't her sister. She never regarded me as being any relation at all.' She was pale and her nerves were being kept under control only by the greatest effort. 'When Steve said they were having a divorce we talked about us. He—'

'There must have been something going on before,' broke in Arthur harshly. 'I seem to remember now. . . .' He paused reflectively. 'At the wedding, he kissed you in a very different way from the way he'd kissed you before. Can it be that you and he discovered this infatuation for one another *before* the marriage?'

'No, certainly not!'

'Steve always liked you a lot.' Again Arthur paused in reflection. 'This breakup is obviously the fault of Steve. And my daughter's the one to suffer.' His face was twisted now, his eyes hard and accusing. Why, oh, why, had she let slip the unthinking words that had caused all this!

Luke was also subjecting her to an accusing stare and she wished she could run from them both, run away all by herself. She had no money and that again was her own fault. Arthur had never been mean and she could have saved from the allowance he gave her. But she had never expected to be in a situation like this. Already through the turmoil of her mind had emerged the reluctant acceptance that she was no longer wanted here . . . not by Arthur or his wife, not by Greta with whom she had always yearned to be close.

'I think I'll go to bed,' she sighed wearily and rose from the chair.

'Not here, you won't!' growled Arthur. 'And not ever again! Luke, take her the devil out of this! Never did I think she'd break up my daughter's marriage!' He looked at Christine with contempt. 'Don't you come back—not ever. Do you hear?'

'Yes,' she answered huskily. 'Yes, I hear you.'

Chapter Eight

Christine looked around the restaurant. Everyone seemed to be in a lighthearted mood, dining in the semilight of candles and muted lamps. The Captain's Charthouse was one of Freeport's most favoured restaurants with Bahamians and tourists alike, the nautical flavour affording it a certain uniqueness and at the same time a sense of cosiness.

'What is it, darling?' Steve was here on a visit after hearing of what had happened and that Luke had taken her, under protest, to Grand Bahama Island, where he had rented a house rather than have her live at the hotel.

'I want to get a job, Steve, so that I can be independent. I shall be nineteen in a week and shouldn't be in this helpless situation. I'm not free; Luke domineers over me all the time. He'd be furious if he knew you'd come over and we were seeing one another. You have no idea what a relief it was when he said he was going to Nassau and would be away for at least a week.' Pale and unhappy, she looked appealingly at him, thinking how very attractive he was with that rugged look and dressed in a white linen safari suit. She was wearing a multicoloured blouse trimmed with glittering metallic threads. The matching skirt was full and flowing with a corded waist which fitted snugly to her tiny waist. Her hair shone, but she did not look in the pink of condition tonight. She had cried much during the past two weeks, feeling desperate and unable to adjust to this disaster that had happened to her. She was deeply troubled that people would be talking on Pirates' Cay, condemning her for something that wasn't true: the breaking up of Greta's marriage.

'You won't tell me what they're saying,' she added when he did not comment on her previous words. 'I expect my name's mud over there?'

'I haven't heard anything,' he said, but she knew he was lying in order to spare her feelings. 'About getting a job—what would you do, Christine?'

'I've no idea at present,' she had to admit, 'but there must be some way I can earn my own living and break away from Luke.'

Steve lifted his wineglass and regarded her youthful face curiously from over the rim. 'Do you really want to break away from Luke, Christine?'

'Of course.' She frowned. 'How would you like to have someone telling you what you must and must not do all the time?'

'I feel sure that Luke thinks only of your own good, Christine.'

'In the past, yes, but this time . . .' She tailed off, half ashamed. 'I didn't want to come here, to Grand Bahama, but he made me and it was only because he intended to keep you and me apart.'

'You shouldn't have told him—'

'He knew, Steve. Luke's so perceptive. I did let it out

to Arthur, though, and that was my undoing.' She took a sip of her wine, watching the dancers in the middle of the floor, a brooding expression on her face. 'I can't believe all this is happening to us, Steve—the whole family torn apart. It's so sad.'

'Greta and I haven't made things any better.' He too wore a brooding expression, but as she watched him closely Christine knew a little access of uneasiness . . . misgiving, almost.

'Have you heard anything from her since you went back home?'

'She phoned yesterday—a few hours before I was due to fly out here. She wanted to see me but I told her I hadn't any time.'

'She wanted to see you?' A frown creased her brow. 'Perhaps she wants to—to make it up.' Something akin to terror seized her. Steve had been so sure and determined each time she phoned him, and yesterday he had said he couldn't bear to be away from her and immediately arranged to fly over to Grand Bahama once he knew Luke had left.

'I shouldn't think so. In any case,' he added in sudden haste when he noticed Christine's expression, 'I'd not even think of a reconciliation. Greta's unbearable to live with.'

'She's still at Cassia Lodge?'

'As far as I know.' He sounded indifferent, she thought . . . and yet . . . He was in a pensive mood, staring unseeingly at the dancers.

'But Arthur isn't there, you said?'

'He wasn't. But he might have gone back by now.'

'I wonder where he was?'

'Greta said he was staying at an hotel, since he

couldn't bear to go back to Cassia Lodge. Personally, Christine, I'm beginning to wonder if he's become unbalanced over this business of Loreen and her boy-friend.'

'Do you think everybody knows about it?'

'Well, she's been away so often during this past year that I should imagine all their friends have guessed there's something the matter. And after all, Loreen's always been a bit of a flirt, hasn't she?'

'I didn't think it meant anything,' mused Christine. 'Some women are like that but it doesn't say they're unfaithful to their husbands.'

'Loreen's different. She's always liked to think she could turn the mens' heads.'

'She's very beautiful, even though she's over forty.' Steve said nothing and Christine wanted to get back to the subject of Greta. 'Is it really true what Arthur said—that Greta's found someone else?'

He nodded but frowned at the same time. 'She said she had, but when she rang she sounded rather depressed—almost as if something had gone wrong.'

'They might have parted, you mean?'

'Could be—' He reached across the table quickly and covered her hand with his. 'Don't let's talk about them, darling.' He smiled and her heart seemed to turn right over. How she loved him! His smile deepened in the silence of their intimacy and that tinge of uneasiness dissolved, leaving her spirits soaring.

'What do you want to say—about us, Steve?' Sudden unwanted shyness assailed her and she lowered her lashes, quite unaware of the delectable shadows cast onto her cheeks. Steve was looking at her with deep admiration when at length she glanced up again.

'I want to marry you, Christine, just as soon as it's possible.'

'Marry . . .' Her heart was full. Rapture flowed over her. 'I knew, of course,' she quavered, 'but to hear you say it, Steve. . . .'

'Meanwhile, though?' His thumb was moving over the back of her hand in a tender, caressing movement. 'What are we to do love?'

Startled, she could only stare for a space. She was not so naive as to be in ignorance of his meaning, but she could not for one moment imagine living with him while he was still married to the girl whom she had always regarded as her sister. True, there was no blood tie, but all the same it savoured of the indecent even to contemplate a situation such as Steve was so subtly suggesting. She shook her head. 'We'll—just have—have to wait, won't we?'

'For two years?' His brows lifted a fraction. 'It's not possible, dear, not the way we feel about one another.'

Again she shook her head. It was the strangest thing but her mind had wrenched itself back to Luke, and the dark warning he had given her. *Watch yourself. Don't go headlong into something you're likely to regret.*

But why should she suppose she would ever regret it? As long as they intended to marry what did it really matter if they lived together meanwhile? No! *She could not!* What would Luke think of her? She would lose him forever, earn his utter contempt where once she had only his admiration and his care.

'Why, oh, why am I so confused!' she cried, not meaning to reveal her thoughts, but the words were out before she could suppress them.

'Because, darling, it's a big decision, but with a little

time you'll become used to the idea of our being together.'

'Luke.' She quivered, and she put her glass down because her hand was so unsteady. 'I can't lose his respect, Steve.'

His eyes kindled strangely as they stared into hers. 'You just said you wanted to break away from Luke,' he reminded her slowly.

She sighed. Confusion assailed her again as she thought of the long and wonderful relationship she had enjoyed with Luke. Caring, dependable, with always a shoulder to cry on. . . . He had kissed her passionately and she had known sensations new and as exciting as they were bewildering. She felt closer to him then, just as if the physical attraction was drawing her . . . drawing her . . . ?

'I feel I shall never break away from him,' she heard herself say and now she thought of Clarice and of the possibility that Luke might one day marry her. But what of Luke's recent offer? 'He asked me to marry him,' she had to say, lifting her eyes in an imploring way as if she were seeking an explanation from Steve. 'I supposed it to be because he wanted to protect me.'

'From me?' Steve frowned now as he added, 'He told me in no uncertain terms to keep away from you.'

'I know. I was there when he phoned you on the night of the barbecue.' Christine broke off a small piece of crusty bread roll and toyed with it absently. Waiters were hovering or moving around; Willie was playing the guitar in his usual superb way. He was singing 'This Is My Island in the Sun.' A request from a tourist. They invariably requested this, or 'Yellow Bird' or 'Mary Ann.'

'I'm a lot older than you,' Steve was saying and his voice sounded a little flat. 'Luke's more right in age for you.'

She said nothing. It was Steve she wanted to marry; in her mind there was no question about that. On the other hand she had a sensation of ice on her spine at the idea of a rift between Luke and herself. They had had several arguments recently over her 'infatuation,' as he still insisted on calling her feelings for Steve, but always it had ended up in her crying on Luke's shoulder, even while keeping secret her confusion.

'Shall we dance?' Steve broke into her reverie and she rose at once, excited at the idea of his nearness. He danced superbly but was not as light as Luke, who was all muscle and supple agility.

She kept thinking of Luke and feeling guilty that she was here with Steve when she knew he would disapprove. Torn between two men, she thought wryly, one whom she loved but was married, and the other whom she loved in a very different way . . . and who was single . . . as yet. Should he suddenly discover he cared for Clarice he would marry her and—Christine wrenched her thoughts from that possibility and brought them back to her companion.

'Are you happy with me, Steve?' something made her ask after she had glanced up into his face.

'Certainly I'm happy!' he exclaimed. 'Surely you have no doubts about that?'

'You looked—well—sort of dejected a few seconds ago.'

'I suppose I'm troubled about the divorce and how long it really will take to go through. Two years is the maximum but it could be through a lot sooner than that.' He smiled lovingly at her. 'And then, darling, you'll have to decide whether or not you want to burn your boats and marry me.'

'I want to marry you,' she assured him seriously, 'but I don't want to live with you beforehand.'

'Why?' he asked swiftly and bluntly. 'What's wrong in it?' He was staring into her face, that curious expression in his eyes again. 'It's Luke, isn't it?'

She nodded her head. 'Let's sit down again,' she said and wondered why the nearness of his body didn't thrill her any more.

She thought about Greta, and the way she stormed when she knew that she, Christine, was going to dine with Steve. One would almost have believed she was jealous.

And where there was jealousy there was love. . . .

'Sometimes in a marriage,' she said, watching his face intently, 'people have to adjust, and it takes time,'

Not a muscle of his face moved to give her a clue to his feelings or emotions. 'You're suggesting that Greta and I haven't tried?'

Tried?

'I suppose that was what I mean,' she admitted, but went on to say, 'It seems absurd, though, that you and she should have to try after only six months of marriage.'

'We ought never to have married in the first place. I know that now. Greta gets bored far too easily.' He paused a moment in thought. 'Perhaps I'm too old for her too.'

'Too?'

'Well, most people would say I'm far too old for you,

wouldn't they? You're not nineteen yet— All right, we'll say you are,' he amended on noting her expression. 'You're nineteen and I'm thirty-five, almost thirty-six. You'll be in the prime of life when I'm on my way to sixty—'

"Oh, stop!' she cried. 'It's *now* that matters, Steve! Why, we could both be killed in an accident, dying together. I don't want to think of age!'

'No, you don't want to face realities, do you?' His voice was tender, reminding her of Luke in his most attractive mood. 'You're so young, Christine, younger than your age.'

'Luke always says that.'

'Luke is right—but then he's always right when it's anything concerning you.'

'He's been my mainstay for many years,' she murmured reflectively.

'When he asked you to marry him why didn't you think seriously about it?'

She stared at him incredulously. 'I'm in love with you,' she said simply.

'But there's a strong bond between you and Luke, isn't there?'

They were at the table again and the waiter was about to serve the dessert course. Christine said when he had gone, 'You don't have any doubts about my love for you, do you, Steve?'

He paused a moment before answering. 'I'd feel much happier if I could be sure you'd cut off completely from Luke. But you've said you don't want to do that.'

She shook her head, confusion sweeping over her again. All was well lost for love it was said . . . and yet, madly in love as she was with Steve, she knew this compelling desire to keep Luke's friendship and affection. For to lose them would be catastrophe.

She found herself changing the subject abruptly, and the question of Luke was not mentioned again during the evening.

Christine was in the swimming pool when Luke returned from his visit to Nassau. She was unaware of him at first and gave a little startled cry when, on glancing up, she saw him standing there by the side, watching her smooth and supple movements in the water. She came to the side; his hand was there, warm and strong, to help her out. She gave a springing jump and landed against him unintentionally. His arms were swift, his intention plain. She felt his mouth on hers, his hands spreading over her near-naked body. The fact that it was wet, that her hair was streaming, did not seem to affect him in the least.

'You're beautiful!' he murmured after he had kissed her. His hand was clenched about her hair and she felt the water trickling down her back, diminishing the warmth of the sun.

'You came back early,' she remarked, wondering why she had accepted his kiss and his caresses so calmly and without being embarrassed by them. Changes . . . Physical closeness . . . She recalled with startling clarity her thoughts on the evening she and Steve had dined at the Captain's Charthouse. She had wondered then if there was a physical attraction that was drawing her closer to him. It was difficult to dismiss the possibility when he was holding her like this, his hands possessive, his whole manner towards her one of mastery. He seemed so confident of her docility, almost as if she were his slave. A smile curved her lips at the idea and he was bound to notice.

'Why the smile, my Chris?' His own smile broadened to betray the sensual quality of his mouth. 'What's amusing you, my dear?'

'I was thinking,' she answered spontaneously and with the merest hint of coquetry, which was unintentional, 'that I might be your slave the way you act with me—I mean, holding me like this just as if you have a right to do so.'

'My slave?' He seemed amused. 'If you were my slave I would then be able to do exactly as I like with you.'

Her eyes flew open. Colour swept into her face as she felt instinctively that there was some subtle meaning to his words. She tried to draw away, shy with him and more confused than ever. His hold was strong and dominating. She stared into those tawny eyes which now held that hint of metal in their depths, eyes that were alert and penetrating, and they compelled her to lower her own.

'I—I had better go in and—g-get dressed,' she stammered, attempting once again to free herself from his hold.

'Are you glad I came back early, Chris?' His question came slowly and distinctly, as though he were mentally stressing it, attaching much importance to it, or, perhaps, to her answer.

She tried to define the tone of his voice and felt sure that although the mockery was there it could not possibly be the sort of *nervous* mockery which it appeared to be. She answered with perfect truth, 'Yes, Luke, I am glad.' And yet she had told Steve that she had had enough of being told what and what not to do. Now that Luke was back he was sure to be giving her orders and making sure she obeyed them.

'I'm gratified that you want me home again.' Luke held her from him to allow his eyes to rove all over her slender body, its skin a lovely honey-bronze colour and smooth as silk. She saw him swallow hard, as if his throat were hurting; she saw the wild pulsation of a nerve against the bone of his cheek. His eyes became fixed on the tawny rounds of her breasts, as if he were fascinated by their firm, enticing thrusts. His glance flickered to meet her eyes fleetingly before they fell again to rest on the delightful swell of her stomach . . . and then she felt his eyes burning through the scanty covering lower down and she had the sensation of his being able to strip it away without any trouble at all. She coloured again but knew the distinct sensation of response awakening in her.

She was sensually enjoying the examination he was giving her!

'I really ought to get dressed,' she managed weakly.

'Is there any need?' with a half-amused lift of one eyebrow. 'It isn't as if you're likely to catch cold, is it?'

The sun was hot and high in the clear azure sky and if Luke had not appeared she would have relaxed on the pool patio in a lounger for a while after coming out of the water. But now she felt she must insist on getting dressed. Luke did not seem to be troubled that the maid he had brought with him from the hotel might be watching them from one of the wide picture windows that faced the swimming pool. In fact, nothing seemed to be interesting him at this moment except her body.

'I flattered you,' he reminded her with faint satire. 'Are you immune to male flattery?'

She darted him a glance. Was there some subtle reference here to Steve? Was he asking if she were flattered by *his* admiration?

'I'm not immune,' she admitted. 'But you, Luke . . . you are changing towards me. . . .' Words could not be formed beyond this because she had no idea what she wanted to say.

'Yes,' he returned, and now his voice was faintly brusque. 'I am changing towards you.'

Suddenly she was frowning at an idea that had flashed into her brain. Could it be that Luke would like to have an affair with her? She knew he had had several affairs, and those that knew about this used to smile and say it was a wonder he wasn't a rake altogether, seeing how eagerly the women ran after him. Christine's eyes swept over him now and she had the impression of lithe strength and vigour, of a certain sensuality about him that pronounced him all male . . . and virile. . . .

He had been saying recently that he wanted her to grow up. She was recalling that incident when he had taken her to his home the night of the wedding. He had certainly had intentions of making love to her, and she had to admit that he would have succeeded but for the intervention of his Jamaican manservant.

So he was attracted to her physically. Looking back on several recent happenings she realised she ought to have known before now. He had wanted to marry her, telling Arthur that it would be a good idea. He desired her body but what of his tenderness through the years, his concern for her and the security she always felt because of his sustained interest in her? Was his heart involved? She shook her head, telling herself that if he loved her he would certainly have told her so. But perhaps he was too proud, aware as he was that she loved someone else. She thrust the idea from her; she did not want him to be in love with her and suffer what she had suffered when Steve married someone else. No, it would be crucifying for her to give Luke that kind of pain!

'I'm definitely going in,' she stated and, taking him by surprise, she ran into the bungalow and, entering her room, she shut the door with an unnecessary little bang.

That evening they arranged to dine at the hotel, at a table which Luke always had reserved for him, right away in a corner where the vague and vast expanse of the golf course was seen through one window and the dark satin sheen of the sea from the other. A candle flickered in its tall red chimney and the flowers in the silver vase were orchids. Christine, radiant in black Laurent pants and a sequin-trimmed evening blouse with a mandarin collar and long full sleeves gathered into wide tight cuffs fastened with tiny gold-coloured buttons. Her hair shone and the honey tones seemed to be accentuated by the light from the candle. Luke was superbly dressed in a loose-fitting white blouson jacket over a shirt of subtle green—almost the colour of hibiscus leaves. His dark hair, thick and strong, waved attractively at the front, above a wide, faintly lined forehead. So distinguished he looked!—with that handsome face which even the scar seemed to enhance at times like this when his mood was serene and settled. Only when he was angry did the scar seem to rise and form a crimson ridge against the deep mahogany of his skin. He watched her with interest and his smile was slow, lifting the sensuous mouth at one corner only.

'A cent for them,' he said in some amusement.

'I just like looking,' she shot back at him with the sort of satire *she* was accustomed to hearing from *him*.

'Many thanks. I'm flattered.'

She laughed and thought: why am I always so happy with Luke when I love Steve? And suddenly she felt herself to be trapped like a captive between two forces, both of equal power, but in very different ways, and that if she failed to discover the escape route from the fortress of one of them, she would be lost forever. She had the strange and inexplicable sensation of straining to hear a voice from within that would show her the way to her own fulfilment. But the voice was an elusive whisper which faded to silence before she could grasp its meaning.

'You're being sarcastic with me again,' she accused at length.

'You imagine things, my child.'

Child . . .

'It's my birthday on Thursday.'

'I haven't forgotten.'

'Oh—I didn't mean—that is—'

'I hope you would be upset if I should allow your birthday to pass without giving you some token of my esteem.'

'You've remembered it for eight years,' she said and her voice was as tender as the glance she sent him.

'A lifetime to you?' He quirked an eyebrow as a glimmer of amusement entered his eyes.

'It's a long time, certainly.' Luke was being handed the wine list and she added when he did not speak, 'A year from now and my teens will be behind me.'

'And with them the tender years . . .' He might have been speaking to himself, she thought, for he seemed to be totally absorbed in choosing a suitable wine to go with the food they had just ordered. 'What then, I wonder?'

A year from now. Steve could be free. Her thoughts sped on to the future when she was Steve's wife; she endeavoured to create an experience in her mind but all was nebulous and she was back to mere thoughts again. The craving for the untold delights which only Steve could give her seemed to have become a lukewarm desire that in any case would never be fulfilled.

Sombre musings—she tried to dismiss them and to be optimistic about the future. To change the subject seemed to be the most sensible thing to do. 'Have you heard anything of Arthur?' She had waited until Luke had made his choice and then ordered the wine.

'I phoned Cassia Lodge twice but there was no reply.'

'Steve said he wasn't living there when—' Too late she broke off, blushing hotly under Luke's interrogating stare. She hadn't mentioned Steve's visit to the island when Luke asked her how she had been spending her time.

'When did you last see Steve, Christine?' His tone had sharpened pointedly. His manner was stern and yet withdrawn, aloof, but yet he was plainly interested in her reply.

'I saw him here,' she confessed. 'He—he came to see me—er—after you had left.'

'And how did he know I had left?' For the first time ever his voice stung like the lash of a whip. 'You phoned him and told him.' It was a statement, not a question, but again he was awaiting her reply; but there was a long constrained pause before he received it.

'Yes, Luke, I did phone him.' Why was she so meek? Why couldn't she tell him that she was free to do as she wished. But was she free? Without Luke's having taken her in where would she be at this moment? Arthur had told Luke to take her away, had declared quite firmly that she was not sleeping at Cassia Lodge that night or ever again.

'So you lied to me when I asked what you had been doing while I was away.'

'Not altogether, Luke. I just—just—' She stopped, misery flooding over her because this evening was being spoiled.

'Just failed to mention Steve's visit,' he rasped. 'Knowing very well that I'd not approve.'

'I ought to be able to please myself.'

Luke's tawny eyes glinted, hard as stone. 'I happen to be responsible for you, Christine! I absolutely forbid you to see Steve while you're staying with me. Do you understand?' he added imperiously.

She threw him a stormy glance as anger and resentment plucked at her nerve ends to set the pulses throbbing in her temples. Never had she known a fury so strong. She forgot her dependence on Luke as she cried, 'I shall please myself what I do! You've no right to dictate to me as if I were unable to think for myself! I love Steve and we intend to marry, so why shouldn't we see one another? I—'

'Lower your voice,' he cut in. 'I'm not being shown up in my own restaurant.'

She blushed hotly under the reproof and glanced around surreptitiously to see if she had attracted any attention. To her relief no one was looking this way. She apologised nevertheless, and added in a much subdued tone of voice that yet carried a certain degree of spirit, 'We must talk, Luke. I want to be able to meet Steve—'

'Is he still on Grand Bahama?'

She shook her head. 'No, he only stayed two days.' Her lip quivered. 'It's not a bit like an ordinary courtship.'

The hard eyes darkened with contempt, matching the scornful thrust to his voice as he said, 'It's hardly an ordinary courtship, is it? Steve's not only a married man but he's your sister's husband.'

'Greta isn't my sister,' she reminded him quiveringly.

'Don't you care about the talk that's going to result if you and Steve are to have an affair?'

'Affair?' she repeated with a swift and angry frown.

'Isn't that inevitable if you and he keep on seeing one another?'

Was it imagination, wondered Christine, or was he having difficulty with this discussion? A sort of dejection seemed to be running through his anger.

'I shan't have an affair with Steve,' she told him quietly. 'He did suggest—' Again she had let her tongue run away with her and she cursed herself when

Luke, pouncing, asked grittingly just what Steve had suggested.

'Tell me!' he ordered when she remained silent. 'What did he suggest?'

She felt the heat in her cheeks and automatically put her hands to them. Her eyes were misted as they met his across the table. 'He said that two years was a long time to wait—if we did have to wait that time. . . .' Why did she always have to obey these commands of Luke's? Always she found herself being domineered over and doing nothing about it. 'Steve thought, quite naturally, that we—he and I—that is—'

'You'd live together?' The smouldering look in his eyes, the taut set of that jaw, the compression of his mouth . . . all compounded to put fear into Christine and she would have done anything to be able to run from him. But where would she run to? Steve? The idea was born, but for the present she was under this obligation to Luke, dependent on him wholly. It was a desolate situation to be in and suddenly she was blinking rapidly to hold back the tears.

Luke said unhurriedly, 'Perhaps we should leave and dine at home.'

She swallowed hard and shook her head. 'I'll be all right.' She quivered.

'We'll leave,' he decided and beckoned a passing waiter. In a quiet voice he said they were leaving and a few minutes later they were in the car, speeding along a tree-lined road which led to the beautiful region known as Bahamia where many of the wealthy people of the island had their homes. The house was in total darkness except for one outside light which was always left on.

Luke had given the maid leave to go and spend the evening with her sister over at West End.

'We should have stayed,' said Christine tearfully as Luke unlocked the front door. 'There's no dinner for us.' Not that she felt like eating, she thought, but Luke must be hungry.

'We'll scrape something up from the fridge.' He closed the door, switched on a light and turned to her. 'Thursday's your birthday, Christine, and you'll be nineteen. Isn't it time you began acting your age?'

'I'm in love—'

'You are not!' he broke in wrathfully and it did seem that he was *willing* her to believe him. 'Steve is not for you, so the sooner you forget him the better. It's a damnable thing that his marriage is breaking up at this particular time—before you've managed to get over your infatuation for him.' He strode away into the kitchen and she followed slowly, an ache in her heart. Life was becoming unbearable! It seemed to hold nothing bright at all. And soon it would be her birthday. Luke was going to take her to a dinner dance at the Captain's Charthouse but of course he would not do so now.

'Are you going to help me?' she heard him say.

'Yes, of course.'

'I decided to leave the restaurant because it seemed you were about to burst into tears.' His tone was cutting as he threw the words over his shoulder. 'I shall make it my business to see Steve tomorrow.'

'You mean—you're going over to Pirates' Cay?'

'That's exactly what I mean.' He was taking a cold chicken from the fridge.

'What time will you be back?'

'Tomorrow? I might not be back tomorrow.'

'Oh . . .' She did shed a tear then, but brushed it from her face with an angry gesture. He was not going to see just how much he could hurt her!

'There's some salad material here. Do something with it while I carve the bird.'

Mechanically she washed the lettuce and tomatoes and put them in a bowl. There were peppers and cucumber but she had no heart for going to the trouble of making a salad. She laid the table instead and they sat down to a silent meal.

Afterwards he said, watching her intently, 'What was your reaction to Steve's suggestion?'

'I told him I couldn't live with him until we're married.'

He seemed to wince as she mentioned marriage but recovered so swiftly that she felt sure she was imagining things.

'And he accepted that?'

'He said I would get used to the idea with time.' Again she was doing what he *wished* and not keeping quiet as she would have preferred to do. This compulsion, this ability to coerce her . . .

'I want to get a job,' she declared suddenly. 'You can't stop me, Luke!'

'I happen to have promised Arthur I'd take care of you, Christine, and that is what I intend to do. I don't make promises and then break them.'

'Arthur made you promise?'

'He phoned me very late on the night I took you to my home on Pirates' Cay. He was contrite but still unable to forgive you—'

'There was nothing to forgive!'

'He believed there was,' returned Luke quietly. 'I made the promise and, as I have said, I intend to keep it.'

'So Arthur does care something about me,' she murmured, for the moment diverted.

'Don't judge him too hard, Christine—'

'Oh, for goodness sake stop calling me Christine! You know that whatever anyone else calls me *you* always call me Chris!' She started to cry but there was no shoulder for her now.

'Is it so important that I use Chris?' he enquired softly, and she nodded her head, gulping back a sob.

'You—kn-know it is.'

A sigh escaped him. His anger had long since evaporated, which was customary. It did not matter how angry he might be, he was always calm again within a very short space of time. But now he seemed to have difficulty in keeping his patience. 'Stop crying,' he said sharply. 'All this misery's of your own doing.' Christine said nothing and he reverted to what he was saying before she interrupted him. 'Don't judge Arthur too hard. He's going through a very bitter period in his life at present. No man enjoys humiliation. Loreen's escapade has hurt him because he loves her, but it has also humiliated him as well, and I suspect that this latter's more punishing to a man like him than the pain of losing his wife. He's sensible enough to know he'll get over Loreen, but the humiliation will be there for the rest of his life.'

'How could she treat him like that?'

'She obviously believes she's in love with someone else.' Luke's voice was harsh. 'He's better off without her, but now isn't the time to try to convince him of it.'

144

'So much happening.' She sighed. 'Everything going wrong for all of us.'

'I've just said that your misery's caused by yourself alone.' Luke's voice was terse but not too unkind. She had the impression that she was trying his patience to the utmost but yet he was endeavouring to make excuses for her. Undoubtedly he thought he understood her, truly believed that all she felt for Steve was infatuation. She remembered thinking of the possibility that he loved her and of her own unhappiness at the idea of causing him the kind of pain she herself had suffered when the man she loved had married another girl.

She said again, 'I want to get a job, Luke.'

'So as to be independent of me?' They were on the pool patio drinking coffee, and Luke was drinking Napolean brandy with his.

'I'm old enough to be independent,' she pointed out reasonably. 'If I hadn't been adopted I'd have been working for two years or more by now.'

He looked at her and seemed undecided. Something stirred in her, then tingled along her nerve ends. It seemed to be an important interlude, as if something momentous was about to happen. She averted her face, heard him expel a breath of impatience, and when she glanced up at last he was sipping his brandy and looking out over the pool to where the light from the bungalow roof picked out the massive bush of magenta bougainvillaea. Fireflies darted about, sending forth tiny points of light to give an added mystery to the intriguing darkness of the garden.

'I can't allow you to get a job yet.' Luke's voice at last and it brought a swift frown to Christine's brow.

'Allow?' she challenged tartly. 'You can't talk like that to me, Luke.'

He gazed steadily at her.

'I can and I will,' he said firmly. 'Leave it for the time being, Chris, just until Arthur makes up his mind what he's going to do.'

'He's retiring; you heard him say so. I can't even go back to Cassia Lodge anyway. And I'm not intending to sponge on you much longer.'

'Sponge!' Sudden fury brought threads of crimson colour creeping along the sides of his mouth. How forbidding he was! 'You're not sponging and you know it. Don't you dare use that word again!'

'You're so touchy this evening,' she complained.

'I have need to be!'

'It's I who should be angry,' she said. 'I'm being dictated to again.'

'Don't try me too far,' he warned softly. 'At this moment I could spank you so hard you'd not sit down for a month!'

She blinked at his vehemence. He really meant it, she thought, and swiftly changed the subject. 'To-morrow—what shall I do on my own?' It was a question that had hovered on her tongue for some time and she had been waiting for a propitious moment in which to voice it. Now was scarcely a propitious time but she must divert his thoughts into some less danger-ous channel.

'Read a book,' he answered briefly.

'I meant in the evening.' Her voice held an uncon-scious note of pleading and all at once he softened. The change was miraculous! But it brought a lovely warmth flowing along her veins. She smiled winsomely in response to the slow curve of his mouth and she said in a low tone, 'You'll come back in time for dinner, won't you, Luke?'

A long silence followed as Christine anxiously stared into his inscrutable countenance. The waiting became almost unbearable; she was puzzled at first and then she knew with absolute certainty that his hesitation was deliberate. He was punishing her by keeping her in suspense. But instead of being angry or piqued she found herself in sympathy with his mood. For she was honest enough to own that she had indeed tried his patience. He disliked her friendship with Steve, genuinely believing it was bad for her to be associating with him because he was still Greta's husband. Yes, mused Christine understandingly, Luke had cause to be treating her like this.

At last he broke the silence, but there was nothing in the mask of his face to reflect his innermost thoughts. 'You'd like me to take you out?'

'Oh, Luke,' she cried impulsively, 'you know very well I *want* you to take me out!'

He smiled faintly but shook his head, as if to clear it. She thought of how easily they always resolved their differences and felt that if all married couples could do the same there would never be any of the heartache and upset of divorce.

'Do you think you deserve that I should alter my plans in order to pander to your wishes?'

She hung her head. 'I've been a little trying—'

'A *little* trying did you say?'

She swallowed uncomfortably. 'Very trying, then,' she amended. 'But I'm sorry and want to be with you in the evening. . . .' She glanced up and he saw the tears

147

glistening on her lashes. He stood up and held out both hands towards her.

'Come here, Chris,' he invited softly. 'My dear, there really isn't anything to cry for.'

'It's not Steve this time, Luke.'

'I know.'

'It's just that I feel emotional. I always do when we have a quarrel. Do you remember, Luke, there was a time when you and I never had a cross word?'

'I remember.' The suggestion of a smile touched the firm outline of his mouth. 'But things were rather different then. You regarded me in the light of an uncle, if I remember correctly—or was it a guardian you wanted me to be?'

She managed a shaky laugh and moved closer to him. She craved the comfort of his arms about her, as they had been about her so many times before.

'We've changed towards one another,' she reflected. 'I want you as a friend now.' She had managed to get as close as she could but his hands were still holding hers, and so his arms did not come around her. 'Why should we have disagreements just because of this change?' she wanted to know.

'You'll understand when you take the trouble to think more deeply about it.' He drew her close and kissed her on the lips. 'I'll get back in time to take you out to dinner,' he promised a moment later. 'Happy now?'

'Much happier,' she breathed. 'And Thursday, Luke? We've always been together on my birthday, haven't we?' She was recalling all the other birthdays when Arthur had taken them all out and Luke was invited every time. 'Arthur always remembered, didn't he? I don't mean my birthday but Loreen's and Greta's too. He never once failed to take us out.'

'Those days are gone, dear,' he said gently, 'so it's best to forget them.'

And Steve, he meant as well—yes, forget Steve because he's not for you. Christine looked up into his face and knew her deductions were correct. She snuggled close and Steve was forgotten in the pleasure of this making up.

'Kiss me again, Luke,' she asked him shyly. 'I'm very sorry for making you angry.'

'We can forget that too,' he decided gruffly, and obliged her by giving her the kiss she had asked for. But this time it was by no means so gentle or restrained. His mouth on hers was moist and mobile and sensuously demanding. She felt the tenseness of the past few hours leaving her and the crosscurrents of dissension had given way to this soothing languor of peace and pleasure.

There was certainly something deep and strong between Luke and herself, always had been from that moment when she had gone to him and wept upon his breast.

'Chris,' he warned softly against her cheek, 'you're trying me in a very different way now.'

But she yearned for comfort, for the full assurance that she had not damaged their relationship. She snuggled close and let her arms creep up and around his neck, shyly caressing his nape and thrilling to the knowledge that she was giving him pleasure. For Christine there was a magical sensitivity to the tender caress of Luke's hands which forced a response in the willing reciprocation of her slender body to the masterful demands of his. She was learning fast, as through her innocence there filtered the knowledge of physical love. A great wave of tenderness flowed into every cell of her body when, freeing one smooth round breast without her being aware of the gentle, tender manipulation of her clothes, Luke spread his fingers around it before taking the little bud and raising it to a peak of desire. Quivers thrilled through her in rapturous repetition as she arched her curves to the masculine hardness of his long and sinewed frame. He was her master, doing what he liked with her, taking his fill of her beauty, caressing every tender curve of her body with infinite tenderness and yet with that innate arrogance which was so much a part of him. She had surrendered and therefore she should be subjected totally. She felt small and helpless . . . and very safe, here in his strong arms, taking her pleasure and giving in return.

'Chris,' he groaned in low and husky tones, 'Chris . . . I must have you. . . .' His hands moved as if freed altogether from the small amount of restraint he had been putting on them, and ecstasy ripped through her as she felt the warmth on her stomach, the bare flesh tingling as a fever of desire took possession of her mind. She had learned that he was an experienced lover, that it was his tender expertise that had aroused her to this point where return was unthinkable. His other hand slid down her back, possessive and warm beneath her clothes; his fingers curved and she was lifted up into his arms. There was no John to thwart Luke's intentions this time, she thought contentedly as she let her head fall onto a broad and welcome shoulder. She slid her hand into his coat, her pulses throbbing in sympathy with the shudder coursing through him.

Luke carried her to the room she occupied and laid her on the bed. He stood above her, fascinatedly watching the rise and fall of her breasts, the gentle swell of her stomach, the trembling mobility of the lovely lips. Her eyes were wide and trusting and a small hand lifted to find itself a home in his. He squeezed it, then, bending, raised it to his lips, his gaze all tenderness, and there was a small throbbing movement in the scar that Christine had never noticed before. He was taking his coat off, and then unbuttoning his shirt, and a shyness came over her because she wondered if she ought to be undressing too. She sat up but he shook his head.

'I'll do it,' he said, reading her mind.

He would do it. Undress her after he himself was naked. Her heart jerked with unwanted nervousness and she was aware of a little access of palpitation.

Then, as if a flash of lightning had entered the deep recesses of her mind to let in the light, she was seeing Steve, the man she loved and wanted to marry! He'd been forgotten completely! Just as if he had never even existed!

She sat upright and drew her skirt down over her legs, then she slid off the bed.

Pale and trembling she looked up at him, aware of the bronzed chest with its covering of dark, masculine hair.

'I can't,' she faltered. 'Steve . . . I l-love Steve. . . .'

She was weeping into her hands as she heard the harsh and scornful words spoken through a surge of quivering anger.

'Steve! You could think of him at a time like this? What kind of a girl are you?' His mouth was curved contemptuously when at last she withdrew her hands and looked up at him. He was slowly buttoning up his shirt. She was overwhelmed with guilt and shame . . . but the sensation that seemed to be rising over all else was that of her mind fumbling through a mist of uncertainty. And suddenly, with a shock of enlightenment, she heard herself say, just as the door banged with unnecessary violence behind Luke, 'It's you. . . .' in quivering wonderment, 'you, dearest Luke, and not Steve at all . . . you were so right . . . it *was* only infatuation.'

Her tear-dimmed eyes were fixed on the door; she was willing him to come back, but she caught her underlip between her teeth as she heard the loud click of his bedroom door further along the passage. Should she go to him and confess her love? The instinct was strong, compelling, but doubts were there too because she had no proof that *he* was in love with *her*. The idea that he loved her had been born but surely if he did love her he would have said so before now? Christine knew her mind was travelling in unprofitable circles, for she had already been through all this and reached the conclusion that Luke would never confess his love while she was infatuated with another man.

A sigh escaped her as she decided not to go to him. She would feel shamed and humiliated if, going to him and offering herself, he should not only tell her he didn't return her love, but he would betray deep pity and concern that she had given her heart where it was not wanted.

What a fool she had been all this time, caring so deeply for Luke and yet not realising it was love she felt for him. She had been steeped in the conviction that Steve was the man she loved and that life would only be complete if, now that his marriage had broken up, she and he could come together.

What a disaster that would have been! For she would have soon discovered that it was Luke she truly loved.

How wise he was. And she had condemned him as being dictatorial and officious because he disapproved of her association with Steve.

What of Steve's reaction when she told him she was in love with Luke? But would she tell him? It would be embarrassing to make the confession and discover that her love was unrequited. No, she would tell Steve only when she was sure that Luke cared, that he wanted to marry her.

Thinking back and recapturing memories and certain allusions made at various times by Luke, Christine felt optimistic and was looking forward to seeing him at breakfast the following morning. She would find some way of discovering whether he returned her love or not.

Chapter Nine

Anna, the maid, was in the breakfast room when Christine entered. She smiled and said, 'Good morning, miss. Are you having breakfast here or on the patio?'

'Here . . .' Christine's voice faded as she saw the one place set. Had Luke set out already to have the confrontation with Steve?

'Where is Mr. Luke?'

'He said to tell you he's gone to Miami and doesn't know when he'll be back, but he thinks he might be away a week.'

'Miami?' A week . . . The colour ebbed from Christine's face. 'He—he gave the name of the—hotel where he's staying?' Was he staying at an hotel? Christine felt he would be staying with Clarice.

'No, miss. He was in a hurry to catch a plane and just left the message I have given you.' She paused a moment, looking curiously at her. 'You'll have breakfast here?'

'Yes—er—no, I'm not hungry, Anna, thank you.'

'But—'

'I'll have a cup of coffee on the patio, please.' She turned and went out to the sunlit patio, seeing nothing of the beauty—the flaring hibiscus bushes brilliant in the sun's slanting rays, the oleanders and opulent cactus flowers, the anthurium lilies and the great mass of other exotic flowers occupying the borders running alongside the pool patio, while the pool itself was clear and blue and she knew it would be warm and silky if she were to decide on a swim. But she had no wish to swim with this weight of depression on her, with this sensation of knots twisting in the pit of her stomach. She was frightened! She felt almost physically ill with the fear that she had lost Luke forever. He had gone to Clarice, the girl Greta had spoken about, a girl whose beauty would have an attraction for any man.

The coffee arrived but it was like bitter aloes in her mouth and she left it almost untouched. Restless and weighed down by misery, she got up and paced about, uncaring if Anna were watching from one of the windows.

'I can't stay here!' she whispered chokingly. 'I *can't!*' Yet where could she go? Luke had brought her here to Grand Bahama Island in order to keep her away from Steve, had done it for her own good, but he could not have visualised a situation like this to occur, where she was obviously going to be all alone on her birthday, alone and more unhappy than she had ever been in the whole of her life.

She went out and strolled around the International Market in Freeport, seeing nothing of all the glamour, feeling nothing of the atmosphere that had previously been so attractive to her. She did not even feel the warmth of the sun on her bare back and arms—in fact, she felt cold, icy cold.

She was crying, and stumbled; someone caught her

and steadied her. She thanked them and moved away, not even knowing if it was a man or a woman.

At lunch time she was still walking, this time having reached the grounds of Luke's hotel. She remembered the time when Clarice was here and she, Christine, had not liked the idea of the intimacy between the two as they swam together in the pool, then sat on the side, close together.

'Why didn't I know then that it was jealousy I felt!' she quivered, tears starting to her eyes again. She became more and more filled with self-pity as the hours wore on. Her birthday coming and no one cared—not Arthur nor Greta, and certainly not Loreen, who, these days, cared for no one except the man who was her lover. Even Steve hadn't tried to get in touch lately—but he couldn't very well phone her when she was living in the house of a man who objected strongly to the friendship.

Desolate and with her feet dragging, she made her way back to the bungalow. Her eyes lighted on the phone as soon as she entered the hall and she decided to phone Steve. What would she say to him, though? She shrugged. It didn't seem to matter what she said so long as she had someone to speak to, just for a few minutes in order to relieve this monotony.

There was no reply from his parents' house and because she just had to phone somebody she decided to ring Arthur. But it was Steve who answered the phone.

'Oh—well—Christine,' he replied awkwardly after she had greeted him. 'How are you?'

'Okay,' she answered casually, and then after a tiny pause, 'I didn't expect you to be at Cassia Lodge.'

'I'm living here—for the present, of course.'

'You and Greta have made up your quarrel?' She supposed her voice must have sounded flat to him but it hadn't been intentional.

'I'm sorry, Christine. I feel the rottenest sort of heel—the way I led you to believe—'

He broke off and there was a tense moment of silence before Christine said, 'Don't apologise, Steve. We both made a mistake.' Her voice was hard and curt. 'I take it you and Greta are all right again?' She was glad of course, but for all that she could not soften her voice even though she tried. 'I hope you can make a go of it this time.'

'Christine,' he said in a voice gruff with contrition, 'I'm so sorry, dear. You're trying to take it well and I wish I were there with you, just to make it easier for you—'

'Steve,' she broke in quietly, 'I have asked you not to apologise. You see, there's no need. I am not "trying to take it well" as you say, because I've no need to do so. I never loved you, Steve,' she went on with slight emphasis. 'Luke always said it was infatuation and he was right.'

'When did you make the discovery?' he enquired interestedly.

'Last night.'

'I see. So you don't feel upset about Greta and me getting together again?'

'On the contrary, I hope you'll be very happy.'

'I wonder if in your generosity you're making it easy for me? I do have a conscience, Christine, and it's troubled me a lot since Greta and I talked and decided we hadn't given the marriage a fair trial.'

'Don't let your conscience worry you any more,

Steve. I really mean it when I say I never loved you. I know it now and had we married we'd have bitterly regretted it very soon afterwards.'

'Greta didn't have anyone else,' he said, ignoring her statement altogether. 'She just said it because her pride was hurt and in order to make me jealous.'

'She herself was jealous that night when you and I were intending to dine together at your house.'

'Yes, I know. I heard all about the scene she caused; she seemed sorry about her conduct but at the same time she was furious with you.' He paused to let Christine say something but she remained silent and he asked, 'Are you all right on your own over there?'

'You know I'm on my own?' she said, puzzled.

'Greta went over to Miami yesterday morning to do some shopping for a couple of days. She phoned me about an hour ago and mentioned seeing Luke a few minutes previously with his girl friend hanging on his arm. They were coming out of a plush hotel, so Greta's guess was that they'd had a night together.'

'Luke slept here last night,' Christine corrected stiffly. 'He left very early this morning on the first plane out.'

'Oh, well, Greta's mistaken, then.'

'She is!' tautly and with force.

'I wonder if there's anything serious in the affair?'

'There wasn't a few weeks ago. . . .' But now? Now Luke might be feeling different. He had certainly been eager to see Clarice, she realised, seeing that he was away so early this morning. Had he phoned her to say he was coming? Yes, he must have done. Perhaps he had even now asked her to marry him. The thought crucified her; she could not continue for the raw feeling at the back of her throat.

'He'll have to think of marriage one day,' Steve was saying, 'but I always imagined his choosing a sweet little innocent, someone docile, too, whom he can domineer over—the way he domineers over you at times, if you know what I mean?'

'Yes,' she said bleakly, aware that she would give ten years of her life if Luke were here to domineer over her. 'Yes, I do know what you mean.'

'Clarice has something, though. She's very beautiful, so Greta tells me.'

'I agree.'

'And Luke's always had an eye for beauty.'

She sighed and said, 'I really rang because I wanted to speak to Arthur. Is he in?'

'He's in his study. I'll tell him you're on the line.' He went off without saying good-bye. Christine pressed her lips together. She felt like an outcast whom nobody had any time for.

Arthur, though, might show some affection for her, she thought optimistically, for he knew now that she hadn't come between Steve and Greta after all.

'Hello,' he said quite affably and Christine's spirits lifted a little. 'How are you, dear?'

'Fine—well, not really, Father. You see . . .' almost without her own volition words came tumbling forth as she bared her heart to him. 'So I've lost him,' she added finally, 'and all through my own foolishness.'

'Lost him? But are you saying he might have fallen in love with you?'

'He could have, yes.'

'Luke's been a father figure towards you far too long, my dear. If and when he marries, he'll want someone new and exciting—yes, if you know Luke! He's far too familiar with *you*, too used to your ways. Besides, he looks upon you as a mere child. No, Christine, you haven't lost Luke—not in that way, because you never had him. However, you'll not have lost his affection either. I guess he'll always be protective towards you even when he's married to someone else.'

She said chokingly, 'He's in Miami at this moment—with Clarice. Greta saw them.'

'Greta?' A small pause followed. 'You've been talking to Greta?' he added in bewilderment and surprise. 'She phoned you from Miami?'

'No, but I've been speaking to Steve just now and he told me.'

'Oh, yes, of course.'

'Luke won't be home for my birthday,' she just had to say.

'Your birthday? When is it?'

'The day after tomorrow.' So he had forgotten her birthday—for the very first time.

'Oh, well—I haven't sent you anything. I'll post you a cheque today, Christine.'

'It doesn't matter,' she returned dully. And then after a long pause during which she wondered if he were still there, 'If I come over will you take me out to dinner, Father?' She didn't quite know the reason for that question because under the present circumstances she had no wish at all to return to Cassia Lodge. 'You're back there altogether now, I take it?'

'I'm selling the business—in fact, it's practically settled already and the prospective buyer's only waiting for the bank to advance the loan. Then I'm going to live with my sister, as I've already told you. I shall be putting Cassia Lodge up for sale any day now.' He sounded a trifle impatient, she thought and bit her lip. Arthur didn't want her even for a short visit.

Yet she said persistently, 'If I flew over to Pirates' Cay today or tomorrow, you could take me out to dinner on my birthday, just like you always did.' Why was she going on like this? She couldn't go over to Cassia Lodge and meet Greta and Steve, not after all that had happened.

The small pause told her all she wanted to know even before Arthur spoke. 'I shan't be here, Christine. I'm sorry. You see, I've already made arrangements to dine with friends.'

'I see. . . .' Her desolation was almost physical, for even though she would not have gone over to Pirates' Cay the fact that she was not wanted there hurt unbearably. 'Well, I expect you're busy so I'll say good-bye.'

'Good-bye, dear. Have a nice birthday. I'll not forget the cheque,' he added as an afterthought.

'Thank you,' she said briefly.

'I'm sorry for sending you away, dear, but I was upset by so many things all at once.'

'I understand. Luke explained—'

'He did? But Luke would, of course. Such a dependable guy, Christine. He'll take good care of you. I expect you'll get a job after all?'

'I hope to get one, yes.'

'Well, don't go too far from Luke. You know how you've always leant on him.' A fleeting pause and then, 'I really must go, dear. Ring me again sometime.'

Sometime . . .

As she was at this moment she felt she would never ring him again as long as she lived.

It was half past seven in the evening when Christine, sitting by the pool with an unopened book in her lap, heard voices and suddenly stiffened. Luke—and Clarice! He had brought her back here with him. Christine stood up and the book fell at her feet. She wondered if she were as pale as she felt and wished the patio lights were a little less bright. Automatically she reached for a switch and tried it. All the white lights went off, leaving the amber ones which were suspended from branches of tall pines, the natural vegetation of the island.

Dusk had fallen swiftly while she had been sitting there but she had scarcely noticed. Now, though, the sky had taken on that mother-of-pearl aspect which fleetingly reigns supreme before the onset of night spreads its spangled mauve colour that rapidly changes to deep purple. It could have been magical, she thought. Christine's ears were alert to catch any words she could.

'Yes, sir, she's on the patio.'

She wanted to shrink to nothingness but instead she was able to step forward as Luke came out through the window after he had drawn back the fly netting. He stood there a moment, looking at her, and she realised that now she was seeing him in a very different light, seeing him as the man she loved rather than the man she had leant upon for so many years. She felt the presence of flutterings within her, the stirring of mind and nerves and heart; she was profoundly aware of his vitality and strength, of the powerful draw of his magnetism, and with a little shock of disbelief she realised that this knowledge of his attraction as a man had been with her for some time. But it had lain hidden away, wrapped in the veil of her subconscious.

'Hello, Christine,' he greeted her impassively at last. 'Have you had a nice day?' The thread of satire hurt as cruelly as he meant it to.

'It hasn't been so bad. And you?' She glanced past him to where Clarice seemed to be giving orders to Anna about a suitcase, and she wondered how long the girl was staying.

'Very pleasant, thank you.'

'Anna said you'd left a message to say you might be away a week.' She was all confusion, with the memory of last night's intimacy superimposed on everything else.

'I changed my mind.' His abruptness only served to increase her discomfiture.

'I phoned Arthur,' she said feebly. 'I wanted to go back.'

'And?'

'He didn't want me.' She looked down at her feet, wishing she had moved away when she first heard the voices, moved into the enfolding gloom of the more wooded part of the garden.

'I asked you not to judge him too hard.'

She nodded her head. 'He was sorry for sending me away.'

'But didn't want you back?' He sounded heartless, she thought, and her heart wept for the times that were gone when all she had from him was kindness.

'He's selling up—the house and the business. It

wouldn't be any use my going back. In any case, Greta's there and so is Steve.' His slow nod of the head made her ask, 'Did you get in touch with Steve?'

'I phoned just before we left Miami. He said that he and Greta were going to try again.' He looked hard at her, his scrutiny searching and faintly scornful. 'So he's lost to you—for the time being.'

Her eyes flew open. 'The time being?'

'Oh, yes, you can go on hoping,' he said with a sort of mocking contempt. 'It's on the cards that the marriage will break up one day. Just depends on your patience as to whether you and he get together or not.'

She said in a voice made husky by unshed tears, 'You're very unkind to me, Luke.'

'Perhaps *my* patience is at fault.'

'It's—run out, y-you mean?' Had he forgotten that he had promised to care for her when she left her home?

'It was bound to, wasn't it?' The sardonic inflection was matched by the look in his tawny eyes. 'Well, Christine, what are your immediate plans now that Steve's made it up with Greta?'

'I—I want to get a job, and a flat. I w-want to be independent.'

'You want to leave here? I'm rather glad about that,' he said. 'You see, if I decide to marry, my wife wouldn't want another woman in her home, would she?'

She shook her head. Was this the man she had known for so long? No, he was different altogether. Unkind, heartless, uncaring what happened to her, forgetting he had said he'd not allow her to get a job. And he had as good as said he was thinking of getting married.

She turned away, her eyes misted as she stared at the serried barrier of water palms that formed the western border of the grounds. It was a charming house, this. Perhaps Luke would buy it and bring his wife here.

'Ah, there you are, darling!' Clarice's voice brought her round reluctantly. 'And little Christine,' she added condescendingly in that acid-sweet voice which made Christine want to hit her. *Little* Christine! Anyone would think she was an infant! 'Luke was telling me you've to stay here for a while because your father's selling up. How very sad! What shall you do?'

'That,' bit out Christine, 'is my business!' She caught Luke's expression and wondered why he was so amused.

'Christine,' he chided gently, 'that was not very nice of you. Please remember you're in my home and Clarice is my guest.'

'I'm sorry,' offered Christine, blushing under the rebuke.

'You don't sound sorry. However, I expect Clarice will forgive you, seeing that your life appears to have been turned upside down. I'll probably be able to help you get a job,' he went on in cool dispassionate tones. 'What have you in mind?'

She glanced up at him suspiciously. His face was a mask, devoid of expression. 'I haven't even thought about it yet,' she said, fear behind the careless inflection.

'I shall be needing a receptionist for the hotel. Perhaps a post like that would appeal to you?'

She shot him a furious glance and was unable to articulate words because of the choking sensation in her throat. She saw the muscles twitch at the corners of his mouth and knew he was suppressing laughter. He was not only being rotten with her he was also laughing at her!

'I'll find my own job, thank you,' she threw at him tartly at last.

'Something upset you today?' he enquired tonelessly. 'You don't appear to be in the best of spirits.'

'I'm fine,' she snapped. 'If you'll excuse me—' She shouldered past him and wanted to curl right up on hearing the laughter that followed immediately on her departure. They were *both* laughing at her!

It was obvious that her supposition that he might love her had been nothing more than a pipe dream.

There were only two bathrooms in the bungalow, and as one was *en suite* to Luke's bedroom Christine and Clarice had to share the other. Christine had told Luke—when she saw him alone for a moment—that she wasn't having any dinner.

'You'll have dinner with Clarice and me,' he told her darkly. 'I'm not having you slight my guest.'

'I'm not hungry,' she began when he interrupted shortly, 'Don't be peevish. You don't like being treated like a child but what do you expect when you act like one?'

'I hate you,' she said slowly through her teeth. 'It's plain that you don't want me here so why can't you tell me to go?'

'I would,' he rejoined swiftly, 'if you'd anywhere *to* go.'

'Oh . . .' Her eyes filled up, blinding her. 'I never thought you'd ever be as hateful as this with me!'

'I did say my patience had run out,' he reminded her softly.

'You—you're punishing me—f-for last n-night, aren't you?'

'Last night?'

'You can't have forgotten!' she flashed. 'You were too angry to forget!'

'So it's only the anger that would remain in my memory?'

Again she glanced at him suspiciously. 'I don't understand you,' she complained. 'You talk in riddles!'

'So you've told me many times before,' was his cool rejoinder. 'I believed that one day you'd make some attempt to understand me but the effort seems to be too much for you—or perhaps it's that you're not interested.'

'More riddles!' she said with a glowering look.

'Let's get back to the question of dinner, shall we?' he suggested. 'I'll expect you to be joining us for apéritifs in half an hour's time.' And with that he strode away and Christine, furiously angry, went along to the bathroom only to find it occupied by Clarice who, by the sound of things, was luxuriating in the water. With a sigh Christine went back to her bedroom to pick out what she would wear. She was doing as she was told even yet again! But how could she defy the man in whose house she was living? He'd as good as said he didn't want her here but he'd not turn her out because she had nowhere else to go.

What a situation to be in! This after the luxurious home she had known for eight years. No home of her own and no job. Suddenly her eyes glinted. She would rectify both! Tomorrow she would begin looking for work, here on Grand Bahama Island.

But almost immediately on this resolve came the picture of Luke married to Clarice and living here. That would be too unbearable, she decided and realised the only course open to her was to return to England, for there she would not only be given help until she found a job, but she would also be four thousand miles away from Luke and his wife.

It was almost half past eight when at last she put in an appearance for predinner drinks.

'I was just about to come and fetch you,' Luke told her crisply. 'What kept you?'

Her chin lifted at his imperious manner. 'I couldn't get into the bathroom!' She glanced at the door through which she had come. 'Where's Clarice?'

'Making a phone call.' Luke flicked a negligent hand and Christine found herself moving towards the chair indicated. 'What will you have?'

'A dry sherry, please.' She leant against the cushions and stared at his broad back. Always he appeared immaculate no matter what he happened to be wearing. At present he wore an off-white jacket of smooth linen which might have been moulded to his figure, so well did it fit. He turned with the glass in his hand and her eyes flicked over the frilled shirt of slate-blue cotton. In the perfection of the slacks was revealed the sinewed hardness of his thighs. Her heart caught as he walked towards her across the wide, high-ceilinged room, self-confidence and majesty in every step he took. As always she saw the poise and maturity of a much older man. At only twenty-seven he had so much before him, and naturally her thoughts flickered to Steve and she accepted that even if they had been in love with one another he was far too old for her. Seventeen years her senior, and he himself pointing out the fact that he would be getting old when she was in the prime of her life.

With Luke all was right . . . except that he was contemplating marriage to someone else. Christine's lip quivered and she saw his tawny eyes narrow, saw the grey flecks take on a metallic quality.

'Your drink,' he said, and for some inexplicable reason his studied civility seemed to widen the gap that had come between them. She took the glass and fluttered him a glance but soon lowered her eyes beneath his steadfast gaze. She thanked him in a small voice and watched him move away and relax his lithe frame in the big armchair from which he had risen immediately on her entry into the room.

He spoke and she answered. Polite conversation which to a listener outside would merely be a general murmur of conventional banalities. Never had she and Luke been like this before. She had always basked in the warmth of his friendship and only now did she realise that she had come to take a great deal for granted . . . had taken Luke for granted. And now he had had enough; his patience was exhausted. He had no interest in her any more. He didn't feel obligated to take care of her.

Clarice came in, her enticing figure clothed in tight-fitting pants of black satin with a matching top trimmed with tiny silver beads. She wore antique silver ear drops and a matching necklace. Luke's appreciative glance took in everything before his eyes lingered with a sort of sensuous speculation on the voluptuous beauty of her breasts. Jealousy stabbed its way into Christine's heart and she was wishing she had defied Luke and refused to have dinner with these two who surely would have preferred to be alone.

'Did I keep the bathroom too long?' A smooth smile accompanied the question. 'I'm so sorry. When I get into a bath I always stay a long time.' Her big eyes swept over Christine in a sort of supercilious and perfunctory examination. 'I hope I didn't inconvenience you too much?'

Christine sent her a scornful glance and at first decided to ignore the question. But suddenly she knew a spiteful urge to embarrass the girl and said with a smile that was forced, 'Not at all; it was Luke you inconvenienced because I kept him waiting and he wasn't at all pleased, were you?' Her big eyes challenged; she saw his lips twitch and realised that he knew what she was about.

'I rather think you exaggerate,' he said. 'I merely asked what had kept you so long.'

'I'm very sorry. . . .' Clarice was put out by Christine's riposte and a thread of colour was creeping into her face. 'I didn't stop to think.'

'Don't let us make an issue of something so trivial.' Although his voice was smoothly cordial he seemed to be having difficulty in controlling his exasperation. 'Christine, another drink?'

Before she could answer Anna came to say the dinner was ready.

It was a silent meal for Christine, who was not brought into the conversation, and as soon as it was over she excused herself and went to her room. Luke had been indifferent to her leaving and this had hurt deeply. He hadn't even asked what was making her leave so early, for it was only half past nine when she said she was going to bed.

Once in her room she could have so easily let the ready tears fall but she resisted the misery that threatened to engulf her. Nevertheless, she felt the need of the fresh air and the peace of the garden and she went from the house silently by the side door. Stars filled the dark sky and she could pick out several constellations as she stood there, at one end of the pool, her neck craned to look up into the flaring heavens. It was strange how she had come to love this island after having lived for so long on Pirate's Cay. She loved this house, too, and thought that Luke, with his ability to have luxurious alterations done to it, could make it into a palace.

A palace . . . for Clarice and himself . . .

She had no idea just how long she stayed outside but when she went in again she was just in time to see Clarice disappearing into the room given her by Anna. On impulse Christine entered the sitting room and stood for a space inside the door, staring at Luke's back as he gazed out of the window. She spoke at last and he came round to face her.

'Luke, I have something to say to you.'

'You have?' Not a muscle moved in the angular mask of his face.

She nodded and said in a low voice, 'I've decided to live in England.'

'With Arthur?' He seemed faintly puzzled now.

Christine shook her head and came further into the room. 'Not with him, no. I intend to get a job there.'

'Why England?'

'It's where I originally came from.'

'That's no reason for going back.' Luke regarded her thoughtfully. 'Why this sudden decision, Christine?'

Christine . . . A little lump rose in her throat. 'Has Clarice gone to bed?' she asked, bypassing his question for the moment.

'Yes; she's just gone, a moment ago.'

'Then—then perhaps I'll sit down while we talk.' She took possession of a chair, watched impassively by Luke. 'How long is she staying here?'

'Is that of any interest to you?' he enquired with a chill and speculative look.

'It's m-my birthday on Thursday and—and I'm not staying here if she's going to be here.'

'You don't like her?'

Christine set her teeth. 'You know I don't!' She glared at him and added, 'She's condescending and haughty and she treats me like a child!' The impassioned speech brought no comment from Luke but a most odd expression entered his eyes. However, he merely asked again why she had made the sudden decision to leave the Bahamas.

'There's nothing for me to stay here for now,' she said desolately. 'Nothing's the same any more.'

'Things don't stay the same,' he said, 'Changes must occur and it's changes you resent.' He spoke seriously and there was no longer any sign of chill or unfriendliness in his manner. 'You can't expect life to follow the same path forever.'

'I don't resent changes,' she denied. 'I know I have to adjust to them, especially now that the home's being broken up.'

'And you believe you can adjust?'

'It will be difficult at first, until I get a job and a place to live. . . .' Her voice faded; she felt a terrible weight of desolation descend on her as she thought of the bleakness of the future that awaited her.

'Steve,' he said and now his voice was clipped. 'He's the real cause of the way you feel, isn't he?'

She hesitated, but only for a second or two. 'I don't love him,' she admitted. 'I know now that I never did love him.'

A long silence followed before Luke spoke. 'When did you find this out?' he wanted to know and again she hesitated. For if she told him the truth—that she had discovered it last night when he, Luke, had made love to her, then with his keen perception he would surely guess that it was him she was in love with.

She couldn't let him guess, not when he was thinking seriously of marriage with Clarice. No, it would be all too humiliating!

'I can't say just when it was,' she lied, avoiding his penetrating scrutiny. 'But I do know now that you were right and it was only infatuation I felt for him.'

'You're quite sure you can't pin down a time?'

She shook her head, still refusing to meet his gaze. 'No, I couldn't say for sure when it was I made the discovery.'

'It must have been very recently, though,' persisted Luke and she said yes, it must have been recently.

'When?' he demanded and she started at the sudden roughness of his voice. 'Answer me! When?'

'I don't know,' she cried, his manner frightening her. 'It just came to me.'

'Was it last night?'

Her eyes flew to his. 'Last n-night?'

'You told Steve today that you're no longer in love with him—'

'You know?'

'I've been talking to him on the phone, remember.'

'You knew all the time, then?' She looked at him accusingly. 'Yet you let me go on—and you asked me unnecessary questions!'

'I was trying to find out—' His voice cut as the door opened and Clarice sailed in, glamourous in a diaphanous negligee.

'I couldn't sleep, Luke,' she said after sending a frowning glance at Christine, sitting there on the low armchair. 'So I decided to come down and have a cosy little drink with you.'

Christine got up at once. 'I'll see you in the morning,' was all she said until, at the door, she turned. 'Good night,' she added and left the room, closing the door quietly behind her.

As she walked slowly to her room she was thinking of the conversation with Luke and recalling that his hardness towards her had evaporated noticeably. He hadn't asked her how she was to get the money for the flight to England. Did that mean he had not taken her seriously? She shrugged away the question she could not answer and yet was instantly asking another.

What had Luke been going to say when Clarice walked into the room? 'I was trying to find out—'

Find out what? Nerves prickled along Christine's

forearms. She felt convinced that what he intended saying was of great importance. And Clarice had interrupted him.

Again Christine shrugged. Whatever it was Luke had been about to say would never be said now, so it was unprofitable to waste her time dwelling on it.

Chapter Ten

Christine was up very early the following morning and
to her surprise Anna handed her a letter.

'It must have come either late last night or very early
this morning, miss,' she said with a smile. 'There's no
stamp on it so someone must have put it through the
letter box.'

Puzzled because the handwriting was Arthur's,
Christine took the letter out to the patio and sat down
at the table. Here on these islands one always had to
collect one's mail personally from the post office boxes
so, as Anna said, this must have been delivered by
hand.

After slitting the envelope and opening out the single
sheet of paper she read:

'A friend was flying over in his private plane, so I
thought it a good idea to ask him to deliver this for you.
He had a car to meet him at the airport, so I knew it
wouldn't be much trouble for him to drop this in to you.
Have a lovely birthday, dear, and do try to forgive me.
Remember what I said about Luke—don't go far away
from him because he'll take care of you always.'

It was signed, 'Father' and there followed three

kisses. She looked at the cheque. Two thousand dollars.

Salvation! She could be away as soon as she could get a flight. And she would have money over to see her through until she landed herself a job.

Wasting no time, she began packing and it was all finished by eight o'clock. Neither Luke nor Clarice seemed to be up yet and Christine phoned for a taxi. As long as she had made her decision there seemed no sense in staying for breakfast.

'Miss,' said Anna with a bewildered shake of her head. 'What are you—I mean, are you leaving?'

'Yes, Anna. Carry that other suitcase out here for me, please.'

'But—'

'Hurry!'

The maid did as she was told and soon Christine was in the taxi and making for the airport. She knew there was a plane at a quarter past nine each morning to Miami from where she would eventually get a connection to London. The flight from Freeport might be fully booked of course, but should that be the case she would call another taxi and go to an hotel. Luke would not know where she was but in any case, she told herself unhappily, he'd not even bother to try to find her. On the contrary, judging by something he had said last evening he would be inordinately relieved to find her gone.

It so happened that the flight to Miami was not fully booked and Christine managed to get a seat on it. Twenty-five minutes later she was on the ground, aware that she had a four-hour wait for her connection to

London. There was an hotel and she went there hoping she could leave her luggage until it was time to check in.

'Leave it over there,' said a porter indifferently after the receptionist had said she could leave it for an hour or two.

'Will it be all right?' She looked at him anxiously, feeling terribly alone and helpless. She had always had someone with her in a situation like this . . . usually Luke—dear, kind, dependable Luke whom she had not fully appreciated until now, when she had lost him forever. Lost him to Clarice who wasn't even a nice girl!

'You'll not be away long, will you?' The porter looked her over with a bored expression. 'Yes, it should be all right there.'

Still troubled, but with no alternative, she carried the two suitcases over to a desk by the door. The porter watched her struggling for a moment and then turned away.

She went from the hotel and walked along, looking at the shops, staring into the bright lights and seeing nothing as her thoughts backswitched to what might be going on at the house in Freeport. Luke would of course have been up for some time now. Anna would have told him of the letter and the speedy departure she, Christine, had made after receiving it. Would Luke have guessed it had come from Arthur, and if so would he have felt obliged to phone him and tell him that Christine had left the house—and the island, because it was only feasible that Luke would have assumed that the taxi was taking her to the airport and that her ultimate destination was England? Yes, mused Christine as she walked slowly past one plush shop after another, Luke would most certainly have phoned Arthur. Was Luke troubled about her? Dejectedly she told herself that, on the contrary, he'd be inordinately relieved that she had gone from his home. Clarice was there with him and Christine could imagine their having had a cosy breakfast on the sunlit patio and perhaps they were now chatting intimately, enjoying each other's company . . . perhaps planning their future. . . .

Giving herself a mental shake and gritting her teeth, Christine resolved to forget them; she had problems and enough without dwelling on what she had lost to another, more fortunate girl.

It was getting time to check in and she went back to the hotel to collect her luggage. The receptionist beckoned to her as she was about to ask the porter to get her a trolley.

'Yes?' she said as she reached the desk.

'There's a message for you,' he said. 'Miss Mead, isn't it?'

'That's right.' Her heart gave an uncomfortable little jerk. 'What is the message?'

It was written down; she took the envelope and stood aside to open it and withdraw the paper with the heading of the hotel written across the top in bold black lettering.

'Stay where you are. Put me to the trouble of following you to England and you'll regret it. I'll be over in Miami at half past two this afternoon.' It was signed, 'Luke.'

A flood of crimson stained her cheeks as she glanced up and met the amused eyes of the receptionist. Had he taken the message? It would seem so. She swallowed and managed to ask, 'When did you receive this?'

'Just after you'd left your luggage.'

'There's obviously a plane due in from Freeport at half past two?'

'Yes, miss. The gentleman said on the phone that he would be catching the two-five from Freeport.'

'I can't think how he knew I'd be here,' she said, puzzled.

'He did say he had decided to try here because he knew you had a long wait and I had the impression that he assumed you'd come here for a meal.'

She thought about this and decided it was logical that Luke would phone the hotel.

'Perhaps you'd like to have lunch while you're waiting?' the man was suggesting and Christine nodded automatically. 'The restaurant's just through there.' He gestured and she moved away, casting an eye in the direction of her luggage and then hearing the man say, 'Don't worry about your suitcases. They're quite safe.'

She sat down at a table near the window and ordered a steak even though she was not hungry. Why was he coming over? Had he felt guilty at not keeping his promise to Arthur? This seemed the only feasible explanation of his action in preventing her from leaving Miami. Not that he *could* prevent her, but as always she was doing as she was told. Always he seemed able to make her obey him, and without much trouble at all. Was she weak in character? Or was it that Luke possessed rather more strength than she could cope with? He certainly had more strength and self-assurance than that of any man she had ever met.

Her thoughts came back to his imperiousness as

regards the message he had left. 'Stay where you are. Put me to the trouble of following you to England and you'll regret it.' Pompous, dictatorial creature! Suddenly she was furious, both with Luke and herself. Why should he think he could dictate to her? More important, why should she be so meek as to let him? For one fleeting moment she knew an urge to get up and check in and let him find her gone when he arrived here from Freeport.

But the idea was short-lived. She wanted to see Luke, wanted him to make her go back.

And yet, what then? He had as good as said he didn't want her because if he married, his wife wouldn't be happy with another woman there. It suddenly occurred to Christine that there was a great deal about this whole business that she did not understand.

She managed to eat some of the meat and a few vegetables. She was having her second cup of coffee when, glancing towards the entrance, she saw Luke standing there, his tawny eyes sweeping around the tables. She felt her heart give a great lurch and her hand was suddenly so unsteady that her coffee spilled into the saucer as she picked up the cup. She put it down with a little bang and half rose from her chair, then sank down again. Luke's face was like thunder and only when he realised he was attracting unwanted attention did his face relax. He came towards her and stood by the table. Christine glanced up into his taut face and wondered if she were as white as she felt.

He sat down on the vacant chair opposite to her. 'Well,' he began in low, gritting tones, 'what have you to say?'

'I received a cheque from—'

'You can skip that,' he broke in imperiously. 'I know.'

She licked her lips. 'I was going to England—I did say that this was my intention.'

'Going—without as much as a good-bye?' The grey in his eyes was like tempered steel. That he was in a furious temper was very plain indeed, and Christine found herself thanking her stars that she was not alone with him at the bungalow. She had never seen him affected by anger to this extent and there was no knowing what he might be tempted to do to her.

'Drink that coffee if you want it,' he ordered peremptorily. 'I've arranged for a car to come to take us to an hotel.'

'Oh . . . why?'

'Because you and I have a lot to talk about,' he snapped. 'Drink it if you must, though it looks revolting to me!' He eyed with disgust the sloppy saucer and the spots of coffee on the white tablecloth. She went red and wanted to cry. She supposed her nerves must be frayed after all that had happened to her—and that was happening at this moment.

'I d-don't want it,' she said on a pettish note that once would have brought a quirk of amusement to his expression.

Now, however, he regarded her with a scowling countenance and said curtly, 'Very well. We'll be on our way.'

The car was there and the luggage was put into the boot.

Ten minutes later they were in the hotel being shown up to a magnificent suite which Luke had booked before leaving Freeport. He ushered Christine in, banged the door after the departing porter who had brought up the suitcases and said without preamble, 'And now, Christine, what the devil did you mean by running off like that without a word?' He stood towering above her, bronzed and masculine and with that familiar air of arrogant maturity which it took so many men half a lifetime to acquire. She felt small and meek and wished she could escape from his intended domination. Then suddenly she was fired with anger and indignation as her mind began to reject his imperious manner.

'I'm perfectly free to go to England if I want!' she flashed with a tilt of her head. 'As for not leaving any message—well, you'd given me to understand that you would be greatly relieved if I left you—'

'No such thing!'

'Oh, yes, you did, Luke. You said you'd tell me to go if I had had anywhere *to* go. Don't you deny it!' she added when he opened his mouth to speak. 'Don't deny anything! You were horrid to me and said you were g-going to marry Clarice and—'

'Clarice? I never mentioned marriage to Clarice!'

'You meant it, anyway. For who else would you be marrying? You said the woman—the girl—you would marry wouldn't want me in the house. And it was easy to see that you and Clarice wanted to be alone so—so I decided t-to leave. . . .' Her voice failed her and she was choking back the tears. 'Why—why h-have you come here?' she managed at last, her voice ragged and high-pitched as a result of her heightened emotions. 'I suppose you're feeling guilty at letting Arthur down.'

'Arthur?' His anger was dissolving rapidly, just as it always did. 'What the devil has he to do with anything?'

183

'You said you'd promised him you'd take care of me—b-but if th-this is taking care—this bullying m-me . . .' Again her voice trailed to silence and a look of pure wonderment widened her eyes. 'Wasn't it because of your promise to Arthur?' she quivered huskily. Her mind was all chaos, for she was remembering her conviction that there was much she did not understand.

'Arthur has nothing to do with my being here, Chris,' he said, and at the hint of gentleness in his tone Christine was filled with nostalgia for the old familiar Luke she used to know, her prop and her guide. 'I came because I have no intention of allowing you to go to England—'

'Allow?' She tried to snap at him but failed because of the wild upsurge of love that was affecting her heart. 'Must you use that word, Luke?'

'I daresay I shall be using the word on and off for the rest of my life,' he said calmly. And unexpectedly he held out both hands. Without thinking about anything else she put hers into them. 'We've been beating about the bush far too long, my Chris.' He drew her to him with a masterful gesture and kissed her hard on the lips. 'I can feel your heart beating. . . .' His strong body succumbed to the call of the flesh and he was quivering against her. 'I'm intending to marry you, Chris, and without too much delay. A fortnight—'

'Luke—what?' She struggled to put a small amount of distance between them so that she could look up into the tawny eyes. 'You said you were intending to marry me?'

'What of it— Oh, darling, I forgot. I'll ask you

instead. Dear Chris, my Chris, will you marry me, beloved?'

It seemed to Christine that the entire world was spinning around her. 'You asked me to marry you,' she breathed. 'Oh, Luke, how did you know I loved you, that I want only to be your wife?' She snuggled close just as she used to do and realised that apart from the fact that she wanted him physically, nothing had really changed. Luke was her prop, just as he always had been, just as he always would be, until the very end. 'Clarice,' she murmured without much interest, 'where is she now?'

'At the bungalow.' Luke bent his dark head and took her lips in a long and passionate kiss that left her breathless and craving for more—*much more!* 'She knows I love you.'

'Is she seething?' Christine touched his chin with her lips.

'Catty little wretch!'

'She wasn't any good for you.'

'I wanted to make you jealous, so I asked her over to the bungalow.'

'Poor girl,' said Christine inconsistently. 'You ought to be ashamed of yourself for leading her on. Poor Clarice.'

'She'll survive. I rather think she always knew it was you.'

'She did?' Christine let her arms steal about his neck and moved her fingers tantalisingly over his nape. 'Why?'

'Because I was always talking about you.'

'But you were horrid to me.'

'Revenge, my love. You'd played havoc with my

feelings for years. I'd had enough. Chris,' he added sternly as he held her from him and gave her a severe look, prolonged and unsmiling. 'I just had to retaliate.'

'You knew I loved you?'

'I guessed. And then when I had spoken to Steve and learned that you'd told him you didn't love him, I knew it was me you really loved and that you'd discovered it last night.'

'As you were closing—*banging*—the door. I suddenly knew it was you, dearest Luke!'

'Why didn't you call me back?' His eyes held a hint of mocking amusement. 'Were you afraid?'

'I wasn't sure you loved me.' She was shy suddenly and hid her face in his coat. 'I thought that if I did confess my love and it wasn't reciprocated—' She stopped abruptly as he shook her.

'If you'd taken the trouble to *think* and to *notice*, you'd have known years ago that I loved you and was only waiting for you to grow up!'

'And leave the tender years behind?' she added when she had her breath back.

'I was going to ask you to marry me last evening but it didn't seem to be the right moment.'

'You were? Oh, Luke, I remember the exact moment. Why didn't you?'

'I have just said, my darling, that it was not quite the right time.' Smooth the voice and with that familiar hint of arrogance. He would never be any different, she realised, and wondered what he would be like at forty. She smiled knowingly to herself. To others he would be forbidding, austere, unapproachable. But to her . . . he would be as wonderfully tender as he was today, her dear, dear Luke, her lover.

'There is a lot to explain,' she said after a while.

'It can wait.' Bending his head, he took possession of her lips, moving his own moistly and sensuously over hers. She pressed close to his hard body, thrilling to the strength and power of his masculinity.

'Darling,' he whispered, his breath cool and clean on her cheek, 'I'd arranged for us to fly back to Grand Bahama tonight . . . but . . . this suite is paid for till tomorrow morning. . . .'

'It is?' coquetishly.

'Chris,' he warned darkly, 'you're asking for a spanking!'

'How long have you loved me, dearest?' She sighed contentedly and arched her body in obedience to the pressure of his hand.

'For years and years—a whole million of them.' His lips sought hers and found them, and for a few passionate moments all was silence. She quivered as both hands roamed in fevered, erotic exploration, one finding the delicate globe of her breast while the other slid possessively into the loosened waistband of her slacks. 'The suite is paid for,' he said again and waited for her response, waited with far less patience than he had waited for her to grow up.

'Dear Luke . . .' She lifted adoring eyes to his. 'If—if you want to—to . . . What I am trying to say, dear Luke is—'

'That you have left the tender years behind,' he filled in for her and she merely nodded her head and snuggled against his breast as she had done so many, many times before.

But this time it was rather different. . . .

Genuine Silhouette
sterling silver bookmark
for only $15.95!

What a beautiful way to hold your place in your current romance! This genuine sterling silver bookmark, with the distinctive Silhouette symbol in elegant black, measures 1½" long and 1" wide. It makes a beautiful gift for yourself, and for every romantic you know! And, at only $15.95 each, including all postage and handling charges, you'll want to order several now, while supplies last.

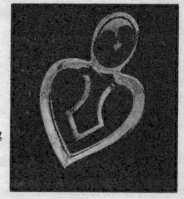

Send your name and address with check or money order for $15.95 per bookmark ordered to
Simon & Schuster Enterprises
120 Brighton Rd., P.O. Box 5020
Clifton, N.J. 07012
Attn: Bookmark

Bookmarks can be ordered pre-paid only. No charges will be accepted. Please allow 4-6 weeks for delivery.

N.Y. State Residents
Please Add Sales Tax

Silhouette Romance

IT'S YOUR OWN SPECIAL TIME

Contemporary romances for today's women.
Each month, six very special love stories will be yours
from SILHOUETTE. Look for them wherever books are sold
or order now from the coupon below.

$1.50 each

Hampson	☐ 1	☐ 4	☐ 16	☐ 27	Browning	☐ 12	☐ 38	☐ 53	☐ 73
	☐ 28	☐ 52	☐ 94			☐ 93			
Stanford	☐ 6	☐ 25	☐ 35	☐ 46	Michaels	☐ 15	☐ 32	☐ 61	☐ 87
	☐ 58	☐ 88			John	☐ 17	☐ 34	☐ 57	☐ 85
Hastings	☐ 13	☐ 26			Beckman	☐ 8	☐ 37	☐ 54	☐ 96
Vitek	☐ 33	☐ 47	☐ 84		Wisdom	☐ 49	☐ 95		
Wildman	☐ 29	☐ 48			Halston	☐ 62	☐ 83		

☐ 5 Goforth	☐ 22 Stephens	☐ 50 Scott	☐ 81 Roberts
☐ 7 Lewis	☐ 23 Edwards	☐ 55 Ladame	☐ 82 Dailey
☐ 9 Wilson	☐ 24 Healy	☐ 56 Trent	☐ 86 Adams
☐ 10 Caine	☐ 30 Dixon	☐ 59 Vernon	☐ 89 James
☐ 11 Vernon	☐ 31 Halldorson	☐ 60 Hill	☐ 90 Major
☐ 14 Oliver	☐ 36 McKay	☐ 63 Brent	☐ 92 McKay
☐ 19 Thornton	☐ 39 Sinclair	☐ 71 Ripy	☐ 97 Clay
☐ 20 Fulford	☐ 43 Robb	☐ 76 Hardy	☐ 98 St. George
☐ 21 Richards	☐ 45 Carroll	☐ 78 Oliver	☐ 99 Camp

$1.75 each

Stanford	☐ 100	☐ 112	☐ 131		Browning	☐ 113	☐ 142	☐ 164
Hardy	☐ 101	☐ 130			Michaels	☐ 114	☐ 146	
Cork	☐ 103	☐ 148			Beckman	☐ 124	☐ 154	
Vitek	☐ 104	☐ 139	☐ 157		Roberts	☐ 127	☐ 143	☐ 163
Dailey	☐ 106	☐ 118	☐ 153		Trent	☐ 110	☐ 161	
Bright	☐ 107	☐ 125			Wisdom	☐ 132	☐ 166	
Hampson	☐ 108	☐ 119	☐ 128	☐ 136	Hunter	☐ 137	☐ 167	
	☐ 147	☐ 151	☐ 155	☐ 160	Scott	☐ 117	☐ 169	

$1.75 each

☐ 102 Hastings	☐ 121 Langan	☐ 135 Logan	☐ 156 Sawyer
☐ 105 Eden	☐ 122 Scofield	☐ 138 Wilson	☐ 158 Reynolds
☐ 109 Vernon	☐ 123 Sinclair	☐ 140 Erskine	☐ 159 Tracy
☐ 111 South	☐ 126 St. George	☐ 144 Goforth	☐ 162 Ashby
☐ 115 John	☐ 129 Converse	☐ 145 Hope	☐ 165 Young
☐ 116 Lindley	☐ 133 Rowe	☐ 149 Saunders	☐ 168 Carr
☐ 120 Carroll	☐ 134 Charles	☐ 150 Major	☐ 170 Ripy
		☐ 152 Halston	☐ 171 Hill

___ #172 LOGIC OF THE HEART Browning
___ #173 DEVIL'S BARGAIN Camp
___ #174 FLIGHT TO ROMANCE Sinclair
___ #175 IN NAME ONLY Jarrett
___ #176 SWEET SURRENDER Vitek
___ #177 THE SECOND TIME Dailey

___ #178 THE TENDER YEARS Hampson
___ #179 MERMAID'S TOUCH Beckman
___ #180 ISLAND OF FLOWERS Roberts
___ #181 MAN OF VELVET Terrill
___ #182 SWEET ETERNITY Clay
___ #183 NO TRIFLING WITH LOVE Stanley

**LOOK FOR _MISTLETOE AND HOLLY_ BY JANET DAILEY
AVAILABLE IN DECEMBER AND
FROM THIS DAY BY NORA ROBERTS
IN JANUARY.**

SILHOUETTE BOOKS, Department SB/1
1230 Avenue of the Americas
New York, NY 10020

Please send me the books I have checked above. I am enclosing
$_____ (please add 50¢ to cover postage and handling. NYS and
NYC residents please add appropriate sales tax). Send check or
money order—no cash or C.O.D.'s please. Allow six weeks for delivery.

NAME_____

ADDRESS_____

CITY_____STATE/ZIP_____

Silhouette Desire
15-Day Trial Offer

A new romance series that explores contemporary relationships in exciting detail

Six Silhouette Desire romances, free for 15 days!
We'll send you six new Silhouette Desire romances
to look over for 15 days, absolutely free! If you decide
not to keep the books, return them and owe nothing.

Six books a month, free home delivery. If you like
Silhouette Desire romances as much as we think you
will, keep them and return your payment with the
invoice. Then we will send you six new books every
month to preview, just as soon as they are published.
You pay only for the books you decide to keep, and
you never pay postage and handling.

— — — MAIL TODAY — — —

Silhouette Desire, Dept. SDSR 7J
120 Brighton Road, Clifton, NJ 07012

Please send me 6 Silhouette Desire romances to keep for
15 days, absolutely free. I understand I am not obligated
to join the Silhouette Desire Book Club unless I decide
to keep them.

Name_____

Address_____

City_____

State _____ Zip_____

This offer expires May 31, 1983

Coming next month from
Silhouette Romances

Dark Fantasy by Laura Hardy

Lisa Hayley, a successful actress, thought she had everything.
Then she met James Tarrant and became involved in a real-life
drama where she longed to make her own happy ending.

To Buy A Memory by Anne Hampson

How could Loretta have fallen for a perfect stranger who
deliberately toyed with her emotions? Yet Paul's kisses were
commanding and soon she found herself past caring.

Love Is Elected by Alyssa Howard

Kara realized she wasn't immune to Matthew Jordan's
charms, but could she really be hopelessly in love with the man
who took her for a wife . . . in name only?

Moonlit Magic by Joanna Scott

Interior designer Timi Johnston had fallen in love with a
Mexican nobleman and found herself in a world where an
independent young career woman definitely didn't fit in.

Sweet Jasmine by Jeanne Stephens

Brook Adamson befriended a lonely little girl—millionaire Dane
Darcy's daughter. But soon that friendship led to a passionate
love for Dane who remained cynical of her motives.

No More Regrets by Dorothy Cork

Once rejected by the only man she had ever loved,
Alida now found herself in his employ—with the attraction
as strong as ever and her heart too willing!